P9-CQI-066

SEQUOYA

SEQUOYA

BY

Catherine Cate Coblentz

DECORATIONS BY

RALPH RAY, Jr.

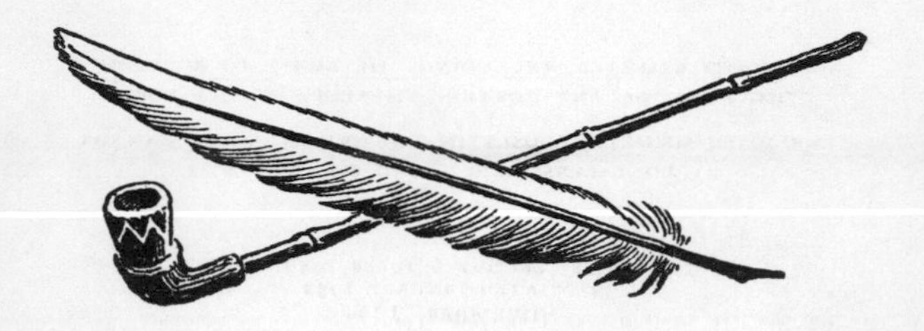

LONGMANS, GREEN AND CO.

NEW YORK · LONDON · TORONTO

LONGMANS, GREEN AND CO., INC.
55 FIFTH AVENUE, NEW YORK 3

LONGMANS, GREEN AND CO. LTD.
6 & 7 CLIFFORD STREET, LONDON W. 1

LONGMANS, GREEN AND CO.
20 CRANFIELD ROAD, TORONTO 16

SEQUOYA

PUBLISHED SIMULTANEOUSLY IN THE DOMINION OF CANADA
BY LONGMANS, GREEN AND CO., TORONTO

FIRST EDITION OCTOBER 1946
REPRINTED JANUARY 1952
NOVEMBER, 1954

PRINTED IN THE UNITED STATES OF AMERICA

To

Sequoya

for whom America's tallest
and oldest trees are named

"They do not gather about the rivers,
they gather the rivers about them."

CONTENTS

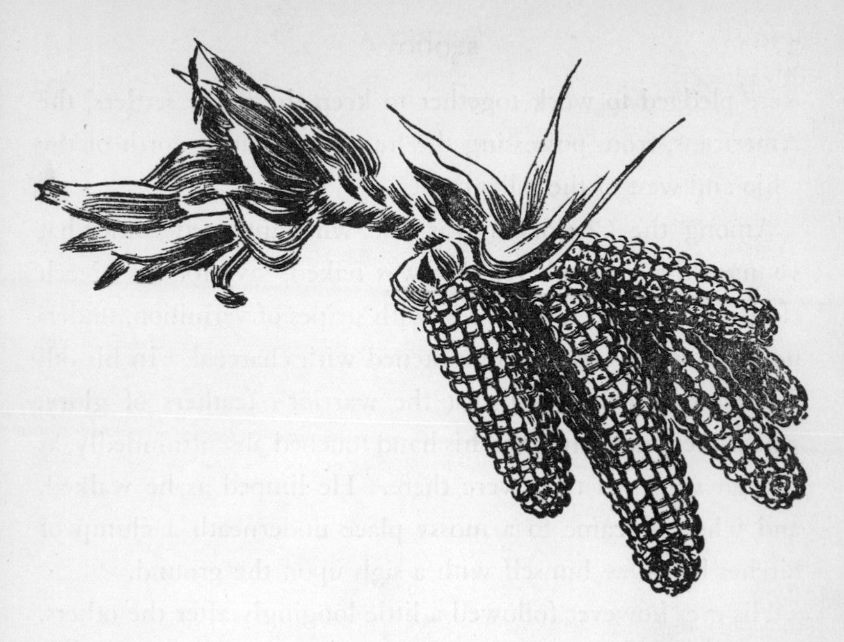

I

The Tribes Rejoice

(November 4, 1791)

THE BATTLE was over and the first sense of jubilation passed. Methodically now the Indians moved among the fallen whites, examining the contents of their belts and pockets. There were murmurs of appreciation when they found good knives. Next to guns and powder the Indians needed knives.

Shawnees, Potawatomi, Delawares, Ottawas, Chippewas and Wyandots were there, and a few Cherokees and Creeks from the south — Indians from tribes as far north as Canada and from below the Tennessee River and along the Coosa. All were pledged to work together to keep the white settlers, the Americans, from possessing the hunting grounds north of the Ohio and west of the Alleghenies.

Among the Cherokees was one who appeared somewhat younger than the others. He was naked, save for his breech cloth, and painted like the rest with stripes of vermilion, underneath which his face was blackened with charcoal. In his oil-dressed scalplock was thrust the warrior's feathers of glory, which every now and then his hand touched absentmindedly, as though surprised they were there. He limped as he walked, and when he came to a mossy place underneath a clump of birches he threw himself with a sigh upon the ground.

His eyes however followed a little longingly after the others, working swiftly and with thoroughness. From their words and gestures he knew they were still highly pleased with themselves. They had a right to be. For here on the headwaters of the Wabash — the entrance to vast hunting and trapping grounds, where again and again the hated Americans had stolen over the mountains to burn the Indian towns and destroy their cornfields, here the tribes working together had won what they must hope was a decisive victory.

At dawn, hidden in the underbrush, they had watched fifteen hundred white soldiers under the leader, St. Clair, parading pompously and precisely in the wilderness. These bordermen had come, as the watching ones knew, to take the village of Kekionga and the carrying place — that portage which formed a link between the rivers leading north and south, as well as east and west! Once that portage was in American hands, the intruding whites would set up their forts along the riverways, and the Indians could no longer bring their peltries the thousands of miles northward to the British garrisons. The English paid the Indians well. They wanted only their furs. The Americans wanted that which was almost part of the Indians themselves — their land!

The drilling was scarcely over when the leader of the hidden ones gave the signal — the clear note of a bird. The watchers had leaped from their places and were upon the enemy from all sides! And now that the morning was but half-gone, it was clear to the Cherokee lying under the birch trees that at least two-thirds of the detested soldiers would never march upon Indian villages again. The other third, including their leader, had fled like rabbits. Let them go! They would tell of the triumph of the tribes, of the many whitemen who had been slain. There would be whimpering among the frontier settlers when they heard.

The loss to the Indians had been practically nothing. A handful of corn grains, a single cluster of wild grapes, the watching one thought, would cover it. Their wounded numbered only a trifle more.

This was a victory, the actions and words of the tribesmen declared, which was decisive. Surely after this day the Americans would cease attempting to penetrate further into the wilderness. They would understand that the Indians would not allow it. The whitemen had taken the eastern lands, but that which lay beyond the mountains — the hunting grounds north of the Ohio, belonged forever to the Indians!

The Cherokee under the birch tree sighed. It was too late, he felt, for the whites to be thus checked. Had the Indians in the old days been wise enough to have banded together when the whitemen had first appeared along the edge of the eastern ocean, they might have held the intruder to the level coastal land.

But not even the Cherokees had realized the danger then. Secure in their mountain strongholds to the south, the country along the ocean had — so the storytellers reported — seemed far-distant. Instead of marching against the whitemen the Cherokees had continued warring with the Iroquois on the one hand and the Creeks on the other. While, almost unnoticed on the east, the Indian tribes along the sea had disappeared, and the newcomers had grown in numbers. Until at last they came arrogantly pushing in upon the Cherokee country itself, pushing and spreading like the searching forefingers of a flood.

The old men had told him often enough how, in the days when *they* were young, the friendship, which the Cherokees had first felt for the intruders, changed into bewilderment. For the whites continually tricked them and forced them to give up one piece and then another of land. Often this was done by members of the tribe who had first been befuddled with liquor and did not realize what they were doing. Naturally the warriors struck back. Yet never did they succeed in reclaiming the land, while trouble rose like dark clouds on every side.

After the very first treaty giving land to the whites had been signed,* some of the Cherokees packed their goods and, taking their families, set out on the rivers and trails for the west. These departing ones declared bitterly before they left that the Cherokees who had started yielding their land had betrayed the tribe. There would be no end, in their opinion, to the newcomers' demands. Finally the Cherokees, the Principal People, would find themselves crowded from the territory they had possessed long before the whitemen arrived. The old men had looked sad as they spoke of those who had gone. No word had come back from them, and they were spoken of as the Lost Cherokees.

But, the old men had declared, the chieftains tried to justify themselves by saying that perhaps it was better to yield some land, for the magic of the newcomers was more powerful than their own. That, the storytellers insisted, was because the chieftains had forgotten one thing. They had forgotten that once there had been wisdom and strength among the Cherokees as great as that of the newcomers. If the Indians had thought more of the old tales and the old ways, they might have remained strong and wise as became the Principal People.

If . . . but what good to think about what the old men had said?

It was far better, the Cherokee under the birches decided, to rest while he could — to stretch out his shortened leg and to warm his shoulders in the sun. The air was sharp for there had been a light sifting of snow during the night. He had been under a great strain then, as he had crept forward with the

* 1721

others, bent over and guarding against a careless step, keeping his ear alert always to the faint signal of rattled deer hoofs — for those nearest depended on his keen hearing.

He was glad they depended on him. He wanted them to do so. Not one of his companions would ever know how difficult for him had been the journey from the Tennessee, how exhausting and seemingly interminable the trails to the Ohio, and then to the Wabash. He would not have let them know — not so long as will and determination could conquer exhaustion.

But now the journey was over, the battle was ended. He had earned the right to rest. That was worth more than all the booty he might have gathered.

Something white was cast aside from a Shawnee's fingers and blew past him. He reached out, caught it, and smoothed it curiously. It was like cloth, yet it tore more easily in his hand. There were some drops of blood on one corner, but scattered over the whole whiteness was a profusion of black marks. They were as plentiful as the tracks of the deer or the buffalo at the salt lick.

The Lame One, who had learned to use his eyes to good purpose, looked now at the blood-bespattered whiteness in his hands.

The Badger and two or three other Cherokees came by and paused. Everyone in the tribe liked this man under the birches. He was the best storyteller they had. Even though he was young the ancient ones had shared their tales with him and he remembered them. Wurteh, his mother, must have fed him some brew more potent than cockle burs to make tales stick so well in his head. Or perhaps in his boyhood wanderings he had found some new plant in the woods which kept imprisoned everything which came to it, and had drunk of its water. The story of this day would be told for a long time. The warriors from the far towns had hoped for such a victory when they came through Tuskegee and had allowed the Lame One to join them.

He held the crumpled bit in his hand toward them now, asking the use of what he had found.

The Badger replied briefly: "It is the whiteman's leaves."

"Leaves?"

"Ha-yu! It is a magic which the whiteman makes. They prize it highly."

"Magic which they put in their pockets — to keep disease away? To keep from being injured? Or killed? Then it is poor magic!"

But a younger Cherokee had other information. "It is whiteman's talk on those leaves. He can be far away and send his talk to someone he has never seen. And that man looks at the leaf and knows what is said. It is as though he heard it with his ears."

"If he looks at it, he must see it with his eyes!" The Lame One was thinking hard.

"Like a signal smoke," ventured another.

"Or a wampum belt."

"Like the eagle tails which we give as tokens of friendship."

"It is a very great wonder!"

The one with the shortened leg frowned. "It is not so great a wonder," he declared. "You think because a man has a pale skin he can do so much better than we whose skins are browned by the sun. This is not so. Look!"

He made a gesture toward the battleground where the heaps of whitemen stirred no longer.

"It requires no great brains to make marks for talk. See, I can do the same thing." He seized a twig and moved to where there was a patch of dark earth, and outlined something in the dirt.

There was a burst of laughter, for he was making the picture of a horse. As soon as he saw it was recognized, he did not finish the drawing. Instead he made a mark beside it and said easily, "The line I have here means a horse. I have made it to mean that."

He drew other marks. One of them wavered up and down like the talk on the whiteman's leaf, which still lay on his knee.

"See, here is talk. I have done it in my fashion. It means, 'There are horses running.' I can put talk on the earth. I can put it on a stone." He broke off the sharp edge of a boulder and drew an eagle, wings widespread, and after it a short quick mark like a feather. "Had I a white leaf like this which the wind brought, and a fine charred stick, I could put talk down as the whitemen do. I, a Cherokee, can do it!"

The watchers laughed once more. Some shrugged their shoulders and slipped away.

The Lame One had heard such laughter too often to be concerned. Laughter and shrugged shoulders were apt to come after he had said, "I can do it!" For there were some things an Indian lame from infancy could not do successfully, no matter how hard he tried.

"I can!" he said again.

Those remaining stared at him, wondering why his tone should be so angry. Was it great matter — these marks on paper? It was a knowledge the whiteman had, a knowledge the Indian did not have. Well, the Indian had other wisdom. Today's heaps of slain showed that, even as the Lame One had pointed out.

Dark fingers caressed the knives they had taken, or touched the scalps hanging at their waists. The blood from these still smeared. One held a watch to his ear, and another set a white wig precariously over his feathers.

But the Lame One did not notice these things, nor did he know when the others went away. He had gone back to the birches and sat there thinking.

Talking leaves! A man could be a long way off and send his talk in black marks on a white leaf. And another understood. They were important, these talking leaves. A runner could carry many of them and not a single message as the Indian runners did, such as Agi-li * had carried in his head when he went far into Canada. In such manner an Indian could make fast what the wise ones among them, all the ancients and the conjurers, knew. Such knowledge could be kept forever.

* Agĭ-lĭ — the gs in Cherokee are always hard.

That must have been the trouble with the Cherokees. That was why they had lost their strength. Some of the old knowledge had been forgotten. Once they had possessed it, but now it was gone.

Forgetting how tired he had been, he rose and began searching. Nearly every dead man had some of the leaves. They were as treasured by the white ones then as knives and money, as important as bullets and whiskey.

As important as arrows and corn, as buffalo, deer, sweet springs and the salt licks were to the Indians before the strangers came; before they had begun crowding the Cherokees westward, out of the eastern mountain land into the Overhill Towns on the Tennessee. Though many of the tribe yet remained in the mountains, near Keetoowah, the town where the Cherokee People had their beginning.

Now there was talk that in time those in the Overhill Towns too would be forced to leave. At Echota, the Cherokees' shining white town of peace and of refuge, even his uncle — Old Tassel himself — had said this.

If they would prevent this from happening, if they would preserve the land they still held, the Cherokees must use anything which the whites possessed — not to become like the strangers, but for their own advantage. Knives and money and bullets were important to the whites. Many Cherokees had learned to use these. And whiskey! About the latter he did not know. Wurteh, his mother, had forbidden the whiteman's drink to him. Someday he would try it. Now he must think more about the talking leaves.

He stared at the white pieces he had gathered. One by one he turned them over. At last, very slowly, he whispered to no one but himself, "I can."

The day had ended. A wolf howled from the darkness. An owl hooted. The first winds of winter blew cold. He remembered suddenly that the winter before, the buffalo, according to the northern hunters, had died in great numbers. The remainder had disappeared. As he and his companions came north to join the tribes, they had found little or no sign of them. No hunter at their towns on the Tennessee or the Coosa had seen a single bull that summer.

Life would be hard for the Indians if the buffalo were indeed gone from the traces. A few years ago there had been vast herds of them. There had been more Indians too, only a few years ago. . .

He stood for a long time, thinking.

He scarcely heard the yells of the tribesmen still echoing triumphantly through the forest, even to the walled fort where the white survivors of that day's battle were huddled, shaking with fear.

Suddenly he turned and went back to the birches and began stripping off great pieces of their bark. It crackled in his hands like the whiteman's talking leaves.

II

A Cherokee Remembers

(Beginning November 1776)

ONE'S LIFE WAS a talking leaf! What had happened, what one had heard and seen was kept for the most part inside a man's head.

The excitement which the day had brought did not lessen for the Lame One with the coming of the night. And so, under the stars, he went over the leaf which was his own life:

He remembered that late autumn when he had first learned the terrifying word — *whitemen!* That was the day when, past the log-walled, bark-roofed houses of Tuskegee — one of the half-dozen Overhill Cherokee towns on the southern banks of the Little Tennessee — he saw a naked Indian clawing the air in his exhaustion as he staggered by. Blood was running from the man's freshly scalped head, and from wounds on his body as well. But by sheer will power he managed to reach the round house standing, higher than the others, in the very center of

Tuskegee. There, at the townhouse entrance, he stumbled and would have fallen. But an old man dashed out and aided him inside.

Almost immediately the watching boy had seen the old man appear a second time and pull himself up on the low-hanging bark roof. Clear to the top he went, giving the sharp signal of warning. And then came his words:

"To the mountains! The whitemen are coming! Be quick!"

There were no men in Tuskegee that day, save the old and the helpless. For the warriors had already heard there was trouble with the whitemen to the south, and had gone forth hoping to meet them and so keep their towns, their women and children safe from threatened disaster. The danger was upon the Cherokees now from the north, and there was no protection against it.

The boy had limped as fast as he could back to his mother with the warning. And he could see clearly even now, the look Wurteh had given her little house. He remembered how she had opened the chest where she kept his father's things, and that she had lifted a coat and held it close for a moment. Then, with great care, she had replaced it. Yet the touch of the garment apparently had made her strong. Her face lightened, her shoulders went back, and she turned to a reed basket and filled it with food. Then she fastened it, together with an extra mantle of skins, to her shoulders, and reached for her son's hand.

Even as they joined the others fleeing from Tuskegee the boy had understood from those last few moments in the cabin. Although his father was white, he was not like these others who were marching toward Tuskegee. Rather was he one whose very coat helped make Wurteh strong and able to face the danger so nearly upon them. The light which had come upon his mother's face when she lifted the coat, still lingered.

Then he forgot about his father, for he saw Agi-li and his mother. Agi-li's mother and his own were sisters. More than ever he envied Agi-li whose two legs were straight and strong. Already he could run like the swift fawn through the forest.

The Lame One had wondered briefly why the cattle — the wacas — were not taken with them. There was no time, however, to ask questions. And Wurteh had no breath for explaining. He was too small to hasten fast enough. Besides, his lameness delayed him. So part of the way his mother carried him. He hoped Agi-li did not notice.

As they fled, a bear crashed almost unheeded through a thicket along the trail. But the boy was reminded of the old song about the mother bear who, when the hunters were coming up the creek, warned her children to go downstream.

Now the hunters were coming *down* the creek, so

"Tsâ' gĭ, tsâ' gĭ, hwĭ'lahĭ.
Tsâ' gĭ, tsâ' gĭ, hwĭ'lahĭ;
Upstream, upstream, you must go;
Upstream, upstream, you must go."

The whitemen were the hunters and they of Tuskegee were the prey. Upstream they were fleeing to the mountains, lest they too suffer the fate at the hands of the whitemen which the Indian who had just warned them had suffered.

The day he fled, the boy had been bewildered, but the night after the victory on the Wabash, lying under the birches and recalling that far-off autumn when all this had taken place, the Lame One understood more fully the reason for the flight — the first the people of the Overhills were compelled to make.

That move against the Cherokees in reality only accented the growing struggle of whitemen against whitemen — the war of the Americans against the White Father across the sea.

The Cherokees had received word of that struggle from the English traders who had come among them, urging them to remain faithful to the old authority. The English, the traders had reiterated, sent the Cherokees trading goods and wanted only furs in return. The Americans wanted land and more land.

That fact the Cherokees already knew. So, for the most part, they decided to remain faithful to the English.

When news of this decision leaked through to the American settlers, the infuriated borderers lost no time in moving against the Cherokee towns. For, they had reasoned, if the King of England possessed such allies beyond the mountains, who knew what might happen? From Georgia and the Carolinas the Americans started inland with muskets, scalping knives and tinder. And, on that day of terror, which the man on the Wabash still remembered so vividly, the messenger had brought word the Americans were coming from Virginia.

He remembered the snakes of smoke which he saw here and there as he looked back over his mother's shoulder. Somehow he understood these came from Indians' houses burning. But most of all he remembered the bewildered fear on the faces of those who fled. That winter, living in a cave in the mountains, he realized there had been reason enough for such fear.

It was so cold! Early every morning he would sense his mother's arm withdrawing. He would be sorry and try to detain her, for he needed desperately the warmth of her presence.

But his mother knew he needed food even more. So before the others were awake she would leave him. He would see her standing darkly in the entrance of the cave. Then, slowly her shoulders would straighten. When they were quite straight she slipped forth.

Somehow or other when she came back she was never empty-handed. She might have some roots she had dug, sometimes from underneath the snow, a store of chestnuts which the chipmunk had hidden, a handful of acorns the squirrels had patted into the earth one by one, or a few winter berries from the vines in the moss. Sometimes she managed to trap a squirrel, or to kill a partridge as the little covey slept, heads outward in a circle. It was meager store she brought daily, but it served. It had to.

That was the winter when he learned to listen carefully. Soon he could distinguish the footsteps and whispers of each one who shared the cave. He could tell the mountain sounds as well — the howl of the wolf and the scream of the wildcat, the hoot of the owl, the call of the wild turkey and the snort of the deer. Sometimes there were signals which might sound like any one of these. But the boy soon learned there was a slight difference. That difference meant they were made by a friendly Cherokee drawing near, a wounded warrior perhaps who must recover his strength.

It was a long winter. Spring came on the day he heard the light step of the messenger who brought word that a truce had been made.

After the Cherokee had given his message there had been a hush in the cave. It was as though those who had lived through the winter could not believe the news. Then voices had babbled together, so the Lame One could not untangle one person's words from another's.

At once those who were able to walk made ready to carry the others. Thus loaded they went slowly and painfully back to Tuskegee. There, for the first time, Wurteh's son saw what whitemen had done.

Every house in the town had been turned into a heap of ashes. Even the small sweat houses, where each Cherokee family slept in the winter, were all destroyed. At first he felt more grieved about these than he did about the loss of the larger houses. During the long, cold hours in the cave he had thought so often of the comfort of a tiny sweat house with the hot coals burning in its center, the furs thick and heavy on the sleeping benches.

Next he discovered that the orchards of peach and of apple trees, which the Cherokees had been quick to adopt from the whites, were gone, their stumps hacked off jaggedly or their trunks girdled. There was no sign of cattle or horses or hogs, only a heap of charred bones, about which not even a buzzard hovered.

Those who had come down hopefully from the mountains, walked slowly, almost stupidly, from ash heap to ash heap. No one said anything. They just walked and looked. When they had seen all there was to see, they stood still.

In a moment, thought the boy, we will go back to the cave.

But a redbird, the tatsu'hwa, began singing, *kwish, kwish, kwish,* in the bushes.

At the sound the spell which had been on the people was broken. An old man lifted his head.

"We are Keetoowah people," he said. "Let us begin building."

"Keetoowah!" That was the name of the priestly clan. It was a name too of the ancient town from which the Principal People had come. It was a word the Cherokees used of themselves. It linked them back with the beginnings of the tribe. It linked them with their gods! It was a good word to say. It gave the people strength.

"Let us start rebuilding!"

Expression had come back to the faces about Wurteh. And the boy understood they were not returning to the cave after all. This town which had once been theirs, they would possess again. The land remained.

In spite of weakness and hunger, they set about the tasks before them, aiding one another in the way they always had. That too was a teaching of Keetoowah.

The Lame One and Agi-li helped. They mixed the clay, with which to plaster and chink the log walls. They gathered stones for the chimneys. Until there were square log houses, roofed with chestnut-tree bark, clustered irregularly about a round townhouse in the center — houses that were not to remain unharmed very long! It was good they did not worry about the future.

That was the summer he had seen Charley Hicks for the first time. Charley lived at Tomatley on the Hiwassee. Like himself and like Agi-li, Charley Hicks had a white father.

Charley had been sitting on a stone when Wurteh's son and Agi-li approached him. The pair circled about, staring at the stranger, for he was dressed in whiteman's clothes, and when he spoke it was in the whiteman's tongue.

"Unaga-whiteman," they jeered scornfully. For even though one had a white father, it was important to remember that one's clan blood came from the mother. It was a proud thing to be Cherokee.

No sooner had the Lame One and Agi-li used the derisive word, than the two wished they had not said it. For when Charley stood up and started to walk away from his tormenters, he limped. Later Wurteh's son learned that this lameness was the result of an accident. It was bad enough not to have two straight legs to begin with, but it must be worse to have possessed swiftness and strength and then to have lost it.

After that day he was quick to notice that Agi-li always checked his own swift pace when he saw either of the lame ones.

As for Charley he put aside the ugly garments, and the three were Cherokee!

The question of food was important that summer, though not so difficult to obtain as some of the old people had feared. There was game in the forest which could be brought down with the arrow. Smaller creatures could be snared and fish caught in abundance. Besides one could cook the food. Food that was cooked was wonderful! That was the spring the Lame One learned how much better was the ache of a full stomach than an empty one.

Corn and potatoes were brought from nearby Echota. For the Peace Town — that Sacred Old Place — had not been touched. The Cherokees were surprised that the whitemen had spared it. From this gift, the people of Tuskegee, working together, planted the town's crops.

The old granary of Tuskegee had of course been destroyed. But someone unearthed beans from a pot in a hidden place. Eager hands cut poles for them. Wurteh's son was not the only one licking his lips that day at the thought of the bean bread which would be baked in the autumn. And, like the others, he counted on his fingers the pumpkin seeds which had been planted near the cabins, and rejoiced when the last one was up.

Anxiously the people of Tuskegee waited that summer for the jar-fly to sing, *tâlû, tâlû*. That meant the beans were ripe. And a little later the katydid announced in a shrill voice that the roasting ears were ready in the corn.

New fruit trees were set out where the old had been. After

a time Old Tassel — the Lame One's uncle — who was Echota's chieftain, came to the door, leading a cow — the whiteman's buffalo, he called it. Soon the cow had a calf. That day, the Lame One remembered, his mother laughed. But *he* was fearful there was something wrong with the small creature, because its legs wobbled so badly. He was glad when they grew straight and firm.

The warriors came home — for a little time. They brought word that practically every Cherokee town had been burned, all the orchards destroyed and the stock killed or driven off. Terrible things had been done by the whitemen to some of the Cherokees who had not fled from their homes quickly enough.

The Americans held long talks with the Cherokees and the older chieftains agreed to cede a large part of their hunting grounds to the Americans.

But the younger leaders and the rest of the warriors refused. These irreconcilables moved away from the Overhills and settled in towns along Chickamauga Creek, where they continued striking against the borderers. The whitemen referred to them bitterly as the Chickamaugas.

Those Cherokees remaining in the Overhills tried to keep the peace, but the warring of the Chickamaugas caused bad feeling on the part of the Americans. So the Overhills were forced to keep alert and ready to flee from danger at any time. Always there was a drummer stationed on the cliffs to sound the signal if need came.

The warrior on the Wabash stirred uneasily. Had he remembered all this that had happened, or had he been dreaming? He was not certain. It had seemed so vivid.

He tried to think now of the second time he had seen his village destroyed. Although he had been some years older when it happened, that second burning of Tuskegee and the flight to the mountains in midwinter did not stand out so clearly. After all, this time the whites were not unexpected.

HE had been with Agi-li then, and the two boys had hidden in the underbrush near a ridge where a Cherokee gave out signals on his drum to those who were fleeing. When the drumming ceased suddenly, he and Agi-li had crept close and discovered that the signal-giver had died from a random bullet. The two boys dragged the body into a lonely cabin and set the building on fire with coals from the hearth, so the whitemen should not know they had succeeded in killing the drummer.

"We must do it for the Tribe," Agi-li had said, and the Lame One forgot his own fear and danger in working for the Principal People.

He was thankful however that this time they did not have to stay through the long winter in the mountains; and that the Cherokees had been wise enough to have provisions hidden against the attack.

Only one thing was worse than before, for the whites had not even spared Echota, the Peace Town. Its destruction was very hard on Old Tassel.

The warrior who was remembering these things shook his head slowly. He could not remember just when the white flag of peace was finally hoisted over Echota, which had been rebuilt, but he knew that shortly thereafter the Cherokees had word that the Americans had won the war against the King across the sea, and that the Americans' Congress, as they called their council of wise men, wished to take the Indian Nations under its protection. That same Congress, however, did not seem to be strong enough to remove the white people who had settled on Cherokee land in the Overhills in defiance of treaties.

As for the Chickamaugas, their towns had been destroyed but the rebellious ones had gone farther south and built yet other towns. These warring ones still would not make peace with the Americans who had taken part of their land. "You will find its settlement," they warned, "dark and bloody."

It was not strange therefore that when the Cherokees on the Tennessee saw how the whites were determined to remain close to the Overhill Towns, there were some young men who declared it was clear the promises of the Americans were worthless. One by one these took their families and began moving farther away from the whites and nearer the Creeks. Some went to isolated places in the valleys and the mountains to the south; some to the new towns of the Chickamaugas beyond Lookout Mountain. These could be reached only by the Tennessee River and by a narrow pass. Nickajack, Running Water, Crow Town and Long Island were their names. While beyond all these was the town which Red-haired Will had started, Willstown in a valley near the Coosa.

A few talked of going even farther away, like the Lost Cherokees of whom their fathers had told, who had gone beyond the Mississippi.

In the old towns on the Little Tennessee there was bitter talk at the council fires concerning those of their number who had not been killed in battle, but had been taken alive by the white-men and were still held as prisoners, or had been sold into slavery.

When the Lame One understood what the word slavery meant, he thought it far worse being a slave than having a lame leg. After all he was free. And what others could do, he could do.

"I can," he said, when the boys of Tuskegee would make ready for a race. Head up, he ran with the fleetest. Season after season he did it, and though he finished last, he was always the first to make ready.

Then there were the ball games. Even now he did not like to recall these. At first he played with the others, but as he grew older he was made to understand that the time for sharing in this sport was over. Playing ball was a serious matter for young men — the brother-of-war, the Indians called it. The honor and often the possessions of the town were at stake. Everyone wagered furiously on the outcome. Sometimes when the opponents were from opposing tribes, the tribes wagered portions of their land as well. That was how, according to the storytellers, the Cherokees had won some of their best land from the Creeks.

Only those players who were strongest, the Lame One was told, should go through the long weeks of preparation, the night of fasting and dancing before the great day arrived. At dawn of that day these chosen ones were taken to the side of a clear river. The medicine men went with them and made long and involved prayers. Then they took a comb of bone made of seven sharpened splinters from a turkey's leg. These sharpened points were set into a frame fashioned from a turkey quill folded four times to make it strong.

Then the medicine men plunged the teeth of the comb deep into the skin of the players and marked them in an intricate pattern from head to feet, both back and front, and from shoulders to fingertips. Blood burst from the lacerations until the sand by the river where the players were standing was damp and red.

But the lacerations would not have hurt, the Lame One was certain, so much as the words which had been said to him when he had been turned aside. He could remember, even now, the ache in his heart. How he had envied Agi-li, about whose playing there was never any question.

He had pretended not to care, and had gone over to the conjurers, bending his head to hear the magic formulas they were mumbling to aid the players of Tuskegee. They whispered these under their breath so that no one should steal their knowledge.

One of these men, however, must have had keener eyes than the others. For suddenly he turned to the Lame One and said, "There is a secret you must learn. Listen! This is what the old man told me when I was a boy. . ."

III

A Story That Was Important

WURTEH'S SON had heard the tale before. But that day he had stared with astonishment at the storyteller when he finished speaking. Even now he could recall how the meaning of the words had burst upon him. They were meant — they had been meant since the beginning — only for him!

"In the old days," so the story ran, "the animals and the birds were to play ball against each other. So they gathered, the animals on a grassy field near the river, and the birds in the treetops near by.

"After the dance, which was always held before the ball game, the birds were preening themselves in the treetops when they saw two creatures scrambling up the trunks of the trees toward them. As soon as they were near enough, the two, who were no bigger than field mice, said they had come to play ball with the birds.

"The Eagle, who was the captain, pointed out that the newcomers each had four feet, so they should play with the animals. But the two said they had offered their services to the animals and the animals had laughed at them. They were too weak, the animals had declared. Why, the animals had such strong and mighty players as the Bear and the Giant Turtle, who could creep into his shell and nothing could hurt him. While the Deer could run like the very wind. The newcomers were told to go off and not get in the way of such mighty players.

"The birds nodded when they heard this, for they knew well enough what strong players the animals had. And they were concerned about the outcome of the approaching game, even though they had the Eagle, the Hawk and the Great Talanuwa on their side. So some of them said the newcomers should be allowed to play.

"The Eagle was sorry for them, but still he did not see how the two could play on the birds' side, for they had no wings.

"All the birds began to talk and twitter, and after much discussion it was decided they would try and make wings for the newcomers from the overlapping edges of the groundhog skin, which was stretched over the dance drum.

"So they flew down and stole these edges from the drum and stretched them in the shape of wings. They added some cane splints to hold them firm and fastened what they had made to the forelegs of one of the creatures. And there was the Bat!

"The Bat was delighted and showed them how he could dodge and circle with the ball and never drop it at all.

"But the other creature was mournful, for after the Bat's wings were finished, there was a not a scrap of leather left with which to make wings for him.

"The birds talked and twittered some more, and finally some of them held the small creature tight, and others seized his skin in their beaks and stretched as hard as they could. By dint of much stretching, while the small creature held his breath and never uttered a sound, even though it all hurt him dreadfully, the birds managed to stretch his fur from his forelegs to his hind ones and made it fast. And there was the Flying Squirrel!

"He took the ball and leaped from one tree to another with it as though it was no task at all. As indeed it wasn't, for his own stretched skin served him almost as well as wings would have done.

"So the game began. The Flying Squirrel managed to catch the ball at the first toss. And he carried it up a tree before the Bear could knock him off the trunk with a swipe of his great paw. Then he threw it to the birds and they kept it in the air for a long time. But finally down it went to the ground.

"The Bear rushed to get it, but the Martin, that clever bird, reached it first and threw it to the Bat. The Bat had been swooping near the ground under the very nose of the Bear, who was the swiftest of all the animal players.

"Yet the Bat managed to grab the ball, and he dodged and doubled, so that even the Deer could not touch it. And finally the Bat threw the ball in between the goal posts. So the game was won for the birds by the very creatures which the animals thought too weak to play with them."

Having finished the story, the storyteller rose and hobbled away without even glancing at the boy to whom he had been talking. The Lame One did not notice. He remained listening to his thoughts and the river for a long time.

There was a way then to overcome weakness — a way to help his side in the game. He thought of Charley Hicks. Charley who, likewise, was lame. He and Charley Hicks were like the Bat and the Flying Squirrel. It was all a question of wings being fashioned.

As suddenly as it had come the glow in his heart was gone. After all there had been someone to help the Bat and the Flying Squirrel. There was no one to fashion wings for Charley or for him. There were only the sidelines, the conjurers and the storytellers remembering and repeating the old wisdom of the tribe.

The old wisdom of the tribe. Perhaps there was the answer.

None of the medicine men had it all. Some knew this formula and some knew that. Some remembered brave stories of yesterday, and some recalled stories so old that they told of the time of the giants and the little folk, of the days in the beginning when the growing things and the animals and the Indians were friends.

The trouble with the medicine men was that each kept his best secrets to himself. His living depended on his ability to heal and to dispense luck in various ways. But, the boy knew well enough, there were ways of finding out this wisdom.

So, after hearing the story of the Bat and the Flying Squirrel, the Lame One began making friends with the conjurers and the medicine men. And when they shared their knowledge, or taught it to chosen young men in a low-roofed asi, he won permission to tend the slow-burning fire in the center. He knew he did not learn the best secrets in this way, but he learned some of them and many of the old stories.

When the medicine men went out seeking herbs he went with them. To the Great-Swamp and the Broom-Sedge-Place; Where-the-Laurel-Climbs-the-Little-Mountains and Under-the-Stretched-Out-Branches-on-the-Mountain-Top; Down-by-the-Great-Bend-of-the-River, Where-the-Foam-Is-Piled, Where-the-Tall-Canes-Grow and Where-the-Brook-Makes-the-Most-Noise. To all these places, and many others he went.

Medicine men were old and did not walk fast. They must pause often to make the proper prayers to the Apportioner of All Things. Besides, when they found the plant they were seeking, or the tree from which they wanted to scrape the bark, they must walk slowly around the plant or the tree, from right to left and from one to four times. Then they must pause and give the prayer asking pardon for what they were about to do.

For each plant they took they dropped a bead in the earth in payment and propitiation. Everything they gathered must be wrapped carefully in deerskin or in a piece of cloth which they had brought. Then the bundle must be taken to the nearest stream and thrown in. If it floated, it was a sign that the treatment would be successful. If it sank, then there was nothing to do but start all over again. Something had been omitted from the prayers or the ritual. Perhaps a word had not been pronounced clearly, a gesture might have been forgotten, or made too quickly.

With different medicine men the boy went, and with his keen hearing he learned their formulas, even the most secret ones. He learned the name of every plant, and what it was good for. He was taken where the rarest ones grew — it-climbs-the-mountain plant, the tassel-flower, the partridge-moccasin, the deer-eye and the water-dipper — and he discovered other and new places where they could be found. For these discoveries the old men were grateful.

Each man had little ways of his own which the boy learned. When he saw a tree which had been scraped of its bark he could often tell from the way it had been scraped just which medicine man had done it.

These scrapings were always from the east side of the tree trunk, for from the east came all that was good for the Cherokees, light and warmth and life itself. To the west lay only darkness and doom and death.

Particularly did the boy notice and look for the scraped place on a crippled tree, or one which had been lightning-struck and yet had lived determinedly on. There was great magic in the bark from such trees which had refused to be defeated. Yet at the same time the medicine men were afraid of the crippled trees and handled their bark with care. Such bark could bring much ill luck if one did not understand how to handle it.

Sometimes whoever the boy was with would stand still for a long time in the wood, head bent on one side, listening. He was waiting for a plant to make him understand that there was the aid which was needed. For in the old days when the Indians had ceased being friends with the animals and had started to kill them for food, the animals in revenge brought disease upon the Indian. Some animals were responsible for one disease and some for another. But the trees and the plants had refused to war against their old friends. They had agreed between them that for every disease with which human beings were afflicted, they would furnish a cure. And if man did not know or had forgotten what plant to choose, in some way or other, the plant itself would manage to let him know.

For a long time the boy had held to the belief that somewhere in his journeyings there would be a plant which would manage to let the medicine man — or perhaps himself — know how to cure his crippled leg.

The men were willing enough to try. Again and again they had used the young fern leaves, those leaves which come out of the earth curled tight, and unroll slowly until they are straight — as straight and strong as a boy's leg might be, if it would only unroll like the fern leaves. The egu'li, the bear's bed fern, they had used, the crow's shin and the beaver's paw — four kinds of fern, blown four times over the body. Four is a sacred number.

Never did he eat the leg of any animal — not even during the starving time on the mountain had he done that. And always he had kept all the rules of fasting and of staying by himself while the treatment and the spell-making was going on. Many times a medicine man had sung over him:

> *"Ha-yi! The Men, the Wizards have gone by,*
> *They have caused relief.*
>
> *Under the earth they have gone by,*
> *As they went they lifted the disease up.*
> *They have caused relief.*
>
> *The Little Wizards*
> *Have gone by under the earth.*
> *As they went they lifted the disease up.*
> *They have caused relief. Quickly!"*

Yet the relief had never come. Wurteh had paid many deerskins and many a pair of moccasins for the spell-making. But nothing did any good. The medicine men were at their wits' end. Finally they all said there was nothing to do but wait.

One was certain *his* spell had failed because, just as the disease was about to leave, a whiteman's cat, the wesa, had come howling and spitting out of the woods. All the Cherokees knew the cat was an evil creature, which was why the borderers cherished them, and always kept one in their cabins. The Cherokees would rather meet a bear with cubs than a whiteman's cat on the trail.

Finally a medicine man from one of the far towns had come. He had tried sweating the Lame One in the asi, dipping him afterward in water where the ice splintered with a tinkle along the edges of the river. But this did no good either. Nothing that could be brewed, no spray from the blowpipe sifted over him, no sprinkling of the medicine from a pine branch, nothing could make his two legs of the same length.

"It could be worse," a blind warrior told him, removing his green soapstone pipe from his mouth, and blowing the smoke of the sumac he was smoking in four directions. A whiteman long ago had gouged out the warrior's eyes with his fingers as the two of them struggled.

The boy agreed. He looked about him, back at the house of his mother, where he knew Wurteh, in bright-colored calico which she got from the trader, was bending over the fire. He even sniffed the good bean-and-chestnut bread baking in the ashes, and he knew there would soon be turkey boiling in the pot, with fat cornmeal dumplings.

He looked at the fields of corn about the cabin. Already they were filled with ears in the milk, and at the foot of the cornstalks were pumpkins turning yellow in the sun. Beyond by the river the cattle were grazing. He saw the milkhouse over the spring where the new wooden milkpans, which he had fashioned for Wurteh, were filled with milk. And he saw the pen near at hand for the sow his mother was going to buy with the furs from his winter's hunting and trapping. It was good to look about him. What on earth would he do without his eyes?

There was a woman in Tuskegee who was deaf. No matter how loudly one yelled, she shook her head and looked dazed. What would he do without his ears? He, who listened and knew every bird call, the bark of the tree squirrel, the laughter of the chipmunk with the stripes along his back, the sound of the wind through the tall trees which the woodpecker loved, the splash of the frog and of the leaping fish, and the gurgle of the brook where he loved best to wander. He could shut his eyes, he was sure, anywhere along that brook and know where he was from the changing sounds.

He had looked down at his leg then. And nodded. It could be worse!

HE looked down at his leg now. There was a grayness in the east. Yo! He had remembered his whole life as he lay on the ground the night after the victory on the Wabash. Morning had come. He realized it was cold, and that he still held the birch bark crushed tight in his fingers.

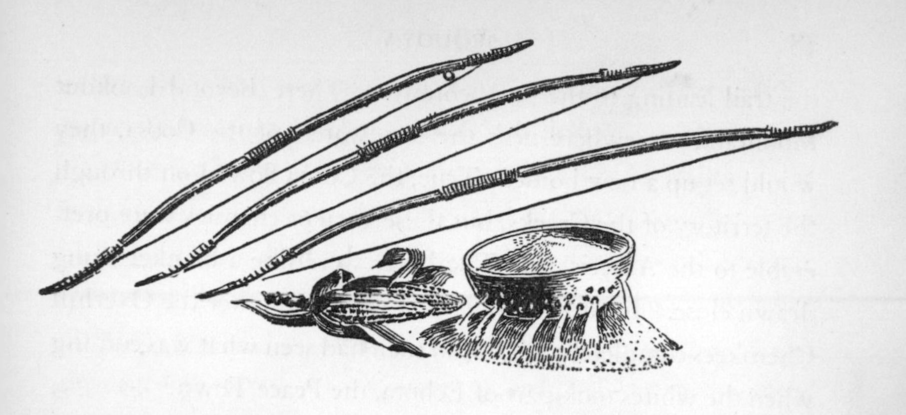

IV

Pictures on Silver

(Ending probably about 1803)

THE LAME ONE had been with the hunters from the Overhill Towns. Now, on his way back to Tuskegee, he reined in along the trail and waited until the approaching horse loaded with household gear and babies, and the half-dozen foot stragglers loaded almost as heavily, should pass. Another family leaving for the war towns, he thought, with a sigh. This was now a frequent occurrence.

The new White Father of the Americans, who lived first at Philadelphia and then at Washington, had adopted the Cherokee Nation, and had set up a blockhouse at Tellico in the very center of the Overhills, with an agent there to spy upon them. The White Father sent plows to the Indians, and looms and spinning wheels.

Yet family after family, with little or no farewell, had taken the trail leading to the back country. There, beyond Lookout Mountain, somewhere near the headwaters of the Coosa, they would set up a new home. True, the Coosa flowed on through the territory of the Creeks, but these ancient enemies were preferable to the Americans. The latter were like a blanket being drawn close. In time that blanket would smother the Overhill Cherokees completely. The old men had seen what was coming when the whites took part of Echota, the Peace Town.

"Do you remember," those who were departing asked, "how Old Tassel protested? How he reminded the intruders that they had promised they would take no more land? *They* retorted that the Indians must learn to live by farming as the whitemen did. But Old Tassel asked why the whitemen should not learn to live by hunting as the Indians did.

"And do you remember how Old Tassel himself, that kindly one, was killed when he answered a call to appear at one of the Americans' forts? And this, though he went under a flag of truce — the white flag of Echota?"

The Lame One nodded and recalled how when Doublehead, who was Old Tassel's brother, heard what had happened, he, with two of Old Tassel's nephews, had departed for the land beyond Lookout Mountain. Before they left all three had sworn to avenge the Beloved Man's death. One of these nephews could not speak of the murder of Old Tassel without crying like a baby.

But that did not bring back the Beloved Man, nor keep Echota itself from being doomed. The council fire was moved south and west to Oostanaula. With that removal went the strength of the Overhills.

"The fire at Oostanaula isn't the same. The chieftains are more uncertain at their councils there. The fire has not burned so long and the land is not so holy.

"Only this we know," the departing ones would insist, "the whitemen are never satisfied. We are going as far from them as we can."

South and west — the way the fire had gone, that was the way many Cherokees were taking.

Thus was the talk of the departing ones. It was always the same. Though sometimes the words remained unsaid. Then the still sullenness spoke louder than words could have done.

When he met any departing, on the trail or on the river, something inside the Lame One cried out to go with them. Instead he would only ask the question, "Where are you going?"

"Crow Town," was the answer sometimes. Or, "Turkeytown." "Willstown."

The words unsaid were: "We are going where there is still game in the woods, where we can live in the old way by hunting. We are tired of being told that we must spend all our time plowing and adding to our herds, as though there were nothing valuable in the world save crops and stock.

"It was not so in the times of which the old men told when we were young. Then the Cherokees could wander far and live as hunters and as warriors should. But now — we cannot go beyond sight of our cabins here in the Overhill Towns, but we meet a whiteman. While some of the Indians are becoming so much like them that often we are hard-put to tell the difference."

The Lame One nodded. He knew what they meant. The way many of the half-bloods dressed for instance. It was as though they were sons of their fathers and not of their mothers, though all children belonged to the mother's clan.

He thought of Charley Hicks. Charley wore shirts of cloth. And once the Lame One had seen him departing for the council fire of the White Father. Then he had worn a hat and trousers!

Shirts of cloth weren't so bad. They were comfortable, though he himself preferred buckskin. But a shirt and a breech-cloth were enough. And a mantle, such as he sometimes wore for warmth. While surely a band of cloth wound simply was the proper headgear. Such the wise men of the Cherokees had worn and their fathers before them. Only the bands then were of feathers or the skins of small animals; the mantles of fur or of feathers from many birds, sewn close together.

As to the incessant land hunger of the whites, this too was at variance with Indian custom. Each man, the intruders declared, must have his own fields and more and more of them. And each man must gather a great store of goods. The more possessions a man had, the greater was he held in esteem.

But the Indians had shared together, and they had possessed the land in this manner for a long time, each man free to use what he needed. It was better to share — it did something to the fire within one, the fire which was from Keetoowah and the beginning of time. Possessions quenched that fire. To be great was to serve the Nation and not one's self. The departing ones were wise.

So, as always, he raised his hand and watched the travelers out of sight before going on to Tuskegee with his furs. Would anyone whom he had known as a boy be left in the Overhill Towns?

Charley Hicks was gone — to Oostanaula where the great councils now were held. And Agi-li — to Willstown. He missed them both, but Agi-li perhaps the most. He saw them sometimes when he slipped in with the other unimportant ones at the council. He kept in the background as much as he could, for he felt his own unworthiness. Charley was usually next the whitemen — who were asking for land — translating their strange and ugly language to the chieftains, translating back to the whites the words of the Cherokees. Charley was a great help to Pathkiller, who would take, it was thought, the place of Black Fox, the Principal Chieftain.

The Lame One smiled wryly. Charley was the Bat of the old story. His wings had been fashioned for him out of the language of his white father. His knowledge of the intruders' language was a great aid to his people.

Agi-li too was always at the councils, for he had been chosen Chieftain of Willstown. At the councils he — like Charley Hicks — was called by the name of his white father, George Lowry.

The Lame One never thought of him so, but as Agi-li, the

runner, the skilful one, who, before the battle of the tribes on the Wabash, had carried a message far into Canada to the English commander there. With such speed and care had he taken his way that no enemy had glimpsed him either going or returning — Agi-li, who was swift as the deer. The story of that Canadian journey had long been told in Tuskegee.

Wurteh's son guided his horse through a stream, and wished he were going in the other direction, with the departing ones to Willstown. But he was not like Agi-li nor like Charley. There were apparently no wings for him. Always it seemed he would remain the Ground Squirrel, taking no part in the game his people were playing against the whitemen. Rather was he busied with unimportant matters.

His mother's cabin was filled with trading goods — hatchets and knives, guns and ammunition, salt and cooking pots, bright cloth and ribbons, a keg of whiskey in the corner. She had trained her son in the handling of these things.

"You must help me with this," she would say. "I am busy at the new loom, which the white agent at Tellico gave me."

So, little by little, as he had grown older, she had drawn him from his wanderings with the medicine men, from his long hours of solitude, and had given him new wisdom with which to occupy his mind. He had learned the value of furs in whiteman's money, in Spanish, French and English coins, as well as an occasional American one. He knew the proper weight of silver in his hand, the ring of good and of bad coins.

But sometimes when there was little or nothing to do, he

would sit on the doorstone and remember that night he had spent on the Wabash. The triumph of the tribes, in what now seemed that long-ago time, had indeed been short-lived. In a matter of two summers the white soldiers had returned, and the American forts went up along the northern waterways.

The English had been pushed out of their last trading posts on the southern shores of the Great Lakes, and had gone northward. The Iroquois had fled into the Englishman's Canada; other tribes — what was left of them — had followed the buffalo westward. On the Wabash and about the Great Lakes, the whitemen built their forts where the villages of the Indians had stood.

He recalled how, when he had returned from the north with the other warriors — mostly Chickamaugas from the Wabash — the sober chieftains of the Overhills who had warned them against going north had counseled louder than ever. It was better, they declared, to turn from the old ways and the old wisdom and take up the new.

The hotbloods in the far towns, however, still believed in following the warriors' path. They were avenging Old Tassel's death, and they continued swooping like hawks upon lonely cabins, or on white travelers along the trails and waterways. Doublehead, Old Tassel's brother, had been one of the leaders in this, and Old Tassel's nephews.

The far towns were a great problem to American frontiersmen. But the whitemen of the border grew steadily stronger, and some of the most bloodthirsty Cherokees were compelled to flee even from the far towns. The Bowl was one of these. He fled with his followers beyond the Mississippi. There was nothing for the Chickamaugas in the far towns to do, but to make peace with their enemies.

Next the report came to the Cherokees that the White Father at Washington — Jefferson was his name, according to Charley Hicks — had said that all the Indians should go beyond the Great River — where the Bowl had gone — and leave to the whitemen the land east of that barrier. One would have thought the Indian had no rights to the eastern land at all. Such an idea was nonsense! The White Father was making loud talk. Surely nothing like that would ever happen. The west was the Cherokees' land of darkness and defeat. All the old stories said so. Surely the Principal People would never go west. Yet — there were the tribes to the north — And the buffalo —

When Wurteh saw that such musing was occurring too often, she would send her son forth to hunt and bargain with the hunters. He enjoyed being with those he had always known, even though every year the familiar faces grew fewer and the supply of furs poorer. On these journeys too he came upon the whitemen more and more often.

There was a loudness in their voices now which he could understand, even though he could not understand the words. Their eyes, their walk, and the way they carried their guns — all this was insult and dare to a hotblood. So the Lame One learned to look at them and not see them. He noticed that this often made them speak the more boisterously and laugh the louder, like a child who knows he is caught in a wrong.

Then, with the hated sound in his ears, he would wonder what the end would be for his people. And he would think once again of the Bat and the Flying Squirrel.

Where were *his* wings? Was it for hunting and trading he had sharp eyes and keen ears? Was there to be no use then for the old wisdom he had learned? For the formulas? And the storytelling? For all the things he remembered?

With the hunters who remained, yes. There he was welcome, not only because he himself had many hunting feats to his credit, not only because he gave them better value for their furs than did the agent at Tellico, but because of his knowledge. They needed the hunting formulas more than ever, for the game was scarce. They were good formulas, that was certain. The man's own record proved it.

He taught what he knew freely, for he was different from the medicine men. There was a dependable prayer, said to the river:

> *"Give me the wind that the game may not scent me, O Great Terrestrial Hunter — the River. Let me search out the game as you search out the leaves and debris and bring them to the Great River. Let me find all the game I need, in the bend of the River. . ."*

And there was one to recite swiftly while the hunter was taking aim. This rarely failed, for it was very old. It went back to the days when the Cherokees' arrows were fashioned from reeds:

> *"Instantly the Red Reed strikes you, in the very center of your soul. Instantly! Yu!"*

The messenger of death must speed forth at the uttering of *Yu!* That was very important.

But with those Cherokees who were becoming like whitemen, there was no time for the old wisdom. They were too busied acquiring possessions.

It seemed to the Lame One that life for him in the Overhills would go on forever, with the alternation between trading and fur gathering, as though nothing would ever change for him, even though all the Cherokees about should depart family by family for the far towns.

But change comes to everyone. Suddenly Wurteh died and the Lame One was alone. It seemed strange that Wurteh would be there to direct him no longer; stranger still that he must decide matters for himself, must live his own life.

Yet habit is a curious thing, and its thongs often hold one fast for a long time after the knot is loosened. He continued his trading and his journeys to the hunters and his life was without any direct purpose until his gaze fell upon U-ti-yu. Then his eyes brightened.

So one morning he left corn on her doorstone, and U-ti-yu pounded it into flour and baked bread for him. By this he knew he was acceptable to her. They were married in the

Indian fashion and there was someone in the cabin again. The Lame One was glad, for he enjoyed having people about him.

U-ti-yu was willing and obedient. She looked to the Lame One to decide important matters. She managed the household and did not demand as many things for herself as Wurteh had done.

As the years passed three boys and a girl, three bows and a meal sifter, came to fill the cabin. U-ti-yu took their presence casually enough. The Lame One provided meat for the family, but U-ti-yu was fond of berrying and of gathering food plants, of drying the pumpkin and peas and putting them away in flat wooden baskets. She was quick and skilful too at the white-man's loom.

Then, as the children grew older, they began doing some of the small tasks. They grew clever with their bows and their fish-nets, so the Lame One discovered to his astonishment that he had more time than ever before. And he himself must decide what to do with that time.

The trading which Wurteh had fostered had gradually grown less important to him. Sometimes he delayed setting forth to collect furs from the hunters. There was no one to interrupt him when he began thinking about the old days and the tribe — no one unless it was his oldest son, Teesy, who would urge him to tell of those far-off times. The Lame One made pictures as he talked. These pictures amused the boy, and the father found pleasure in drawing them in the dirt and on the boulders.

It was this pleasure in picture-making which was responsible for his first interest in the silversmiths. He began noticing their work, and soon realized that some were much better at their craft than others. After that, when he made trips after furs, he visited the best smiths. He examined everything they made with care. There were the armbands of the chieftain, Chuleo, for instance. Chuleo was a show-off and wore scarlet feathers in his headband, while he covered himself with silver from his wrists to his shoulders. He was a sight worth seeing!

Then one day the Lame One looked for a long time at the store of large Spanish coins which Wurteh had hidden away. When he made his next journey it was not after furs.

He went straight to the silversmiths. From one he bought a hammer and from another bits of sharpened steel. He came home and built a slow fire on a stone and melted some of the silver coins in a crucible. From the melted silver he made breastplates, armbands better than Chuleo wore, and earrings — for the older men were fond of hanging great rings in their ears, rings which glinted beneath the wound headbands. Some of them wore a ring hanging from the nose. They were pleased with the animals and the other designs which the Lame One put upon his silverwork.

He hammered a pair of armbands for Doublehead, the brother of Old Tassel, with pictures of an eagle, wings widespread, on each. Doublehead was very proud of these and wore them on great occasions.

The Lame One was happier than he had ever been. He labored from morning to night. He found pleasure in thinking of what he would make and at seeing his thoughts take form in the metal. He took more and more pains with his designs. Sometimes he used his knife and cut the designs first on the smooth inner bark of a sycamore tree. He thought of all the silversmiths among the Principal People who had found satisfaction in this work. As his hands were busy at the task he sensed a new tie with Keetoowah and the beginning of things. He forgot to be concerned about the Tribe, or to ponder over the matter of wings for the ground squirrel.

After he finished some piece of which he was particularly proud, he would tell stories for hours. He told them now better than before and many came to listen. Teesy, his oldest son, was a storyteller too.

The Lame One had spread out some of his best work before him on the morning that Charley Hicks came by. Charley examined the pieces with care, nodding with pleasure at the designs in the metal.

"Astu-tsi-ki' — very good," he said, putting down the last piece. "You are the best silversmith among our people. I have heard this was so, and now I have seen what you have done, I know it for myself. You should sign a name to these pieces."

"A name. Why?"

"I will tell you. I have come from a council at Tellico. Doublehead was there, Little Turkey, Glass, Bloody Fellow, Boot and others whom you know. We sat on some fence rails, piled in a square outside the council house, for it was very hot.

We fanned ourselves with turkeywings and listened to some whitemen who want to come and live among us. They want to teach us of their God, but the chieftains were not interested in the God of the whitemen. Does a fish live on the ground? Or birds in the water?

"Some of the chieftains thought however it would be a good idea if these whitemen would come and teach our children the things which white children learn in school. They said our children would need such knowledge if they must do business with white neighbors when they are grown.

"There was much talk and some chiefs among the Overhills men said, 'Yes,' to this idea, but those from the far towns said, 'No.' Everything seemed about to come to naught, and the Cherokees would not have cared much if it had. Then one of the whitemen pleased them. He began drawing pictures of the chieftains, first of one, then of another. To each picture he signed his name.

"I asked him why, and he said that whitemen put their names on those things which they are proud of making, and the memory of who made that thing is kept forever. Is a Cherokee's name not as well worth keeping on silver as that of a whiteman on a piece of paper with a picture — even though the picture be that of a chieftain?"

The silversmith looked at the speaker and considered the matter.

"When I make talk on paper at the councils for the whitemen,

I put down my name," said Charley Hicks. "I am proud I can do it."

The silversmith thought a little longer. He knew from John Jolly, who lived at Hiwassee, that Hicks could write down the whiteman's language as well as speak it. He did this often for the whitemen at the councils. Most Cherokees could only make a mark like two sticks laid one over the other.

"Write my name," he said at length. "And I will put it on what I make."

The other hesitated. "What was your father's name?"

"Gist," said the crippled one. "He was the Cherokee's friend, and became one of us. He was given land when he dwelt with the Cherokees. Old Tassel spoke well of him."

The other tried vainly to recall such a one. At last his face cleared. He had remembered a trader of whom he had heard in his youth, a no-account by the name of Guess — George Guess. He did not remember that this whiteman was either liked or trusted. While, as for giving him land, there had been, he was certain, no transaction like that. Still, it might have been this man, Guess, to whom the silversmith referred.

In the days when Wurteh was young, there was another whiteman among the Cherokees, the son of an early explorer, and a man whom the Cherokees had trusted and to whom they had indeed given land. Later he had left them and had gone on the staff of the White Chieftain, George Washington. This trusted one had great names among his fathers, and was to father great names himself. It seems likely he fathered Wurteh's son as well. But of this no one can say with certainty. The name of that one was Nathaniel Gist.

Charley Hicks opened the gourd of ink which hung at his belt, and took a quill from a case. Slowly he sharpened the end to a point, split it, and dipped it into the ink.

The silversmith watched the whole proceeding curiously. He leaned close as the other wrote: *George Guess.*

Wurteh could have told. But Wurteh was dead. And her son had only a memory of a word he had heard his mother say. It sounded something like the word Charley Hicks pronounced aloud, when he finished writing — not the way the Lame One remembered exactly, but the sounds were similar: *Guess.*

After the writer had gone the silversmith looked at the paper. Here were pictures — whitemen's talk, designs that he would be able to copy. He, like Charley Hicks and George Lowry, had a whiteman's name now for use at the councils. Because it was — as he thought — his father's name, he wanted it.

But the name did not make him white, he told himself fiercely. He was Cherokee as his mother had been, and of the Red Paint Clan, which was her clan. Never would he have taken a white name — as some Indians did — to which he had no claim.

The Lame One could not know that the men who had fathered many an influential Cherokee, those leaders of whom the Principal People were proud, were whitemen with backgrounds and training far different from many of those who crowded the Cherokees now. Those first whitemen to come among them had been Irish and Scotch, high adventurers and of good family, and some of the best of the early American settlers. Nathaniel Gist was from Virginia. But Wurteh's son did understand that the blood of white fathers had strengthened the pride of their sons in their mothers' race, had stimulated, rather than diminished, the zeal for the mothers' clan.

V

Agi-li Breaks the Dark Spell

(Period ending about 1810)

THE LAME ONE enjoyed his work. The days often were not long enough for him to accomplish all that he wished. To see an object in his mind, and to fashion what he saw with his hands, to make his designs with care, so that Cherokee faces lighted when they regarded them — all this was worth the effort he gave. It did not matter that the gain was not so much as it had been in trading. This was something more worthwhile than gain. He was happiest when the call for what he made was the greatest, and when he worked the hardest.

Yet, imperceptibly at first, the demand for such trinkets diminished. One reason was that he had supplied those Indians who desired armbands and earrings; and the other was that so many of the Cherokees in the towns near Echota where the council fire had been were living as the whitemen about them lived. These Indians had other needs.

"Now if you could only mend an axe or fix a broken musket," suggested one of his neighbors to the Lame One. "Being a blacksmith is not so different from being a silversmith. But it is more useful."

The silversmith looked at the speaker. Then, making no reply, he returned to the design he had been planning.

Again and again some Cherokee would speak longingly of the help a blacksmith might be to the tribe. After such words had been said, the Lame One would work more slowly at his task. Occasionally he did something he had not done before. To forget the words, he would turn to the keg of whiskey, which was still part of his now meager trading stock. After the burning draught, he worked more briskly on the silver — for a time. Yet the next day, or the next, he would remember the words which had been spoken.

Finally one morning he did not take up his work as usual, although he had an order from a medicine man for a nose ring. Instead, with a brief word to U-ti-yu, he went out and saddled his horse. The Lame One had come to a decision — a man should not spend his time doing that which was pleasing to himself. He must work for the tribe. He was bound for the nearest smithy, where a whiteman had set up his forge.

When he reached the place he reined in and sat under the shadow of a tree watching. Day after day he did this, sometimes going inside, sometimes remaining on horseback. No one paid any attention to him as he eyed intently the movements of the blacksmith heating his tools, shoeing horses or an occasional ox; or fixing the rim of a wagonwheel.

At length the Lame One decided he had seen enough. So he bargained with the smith for what he thought he would need most. With these tools and a supply of iron and steel in a borrowed wagon, he returned to Tuskegee. He made another journey to purchase bricks with which to set up his forge. After this was ready, the first things he fashioned were a bellows and some additional tools.

Now he could shoe his neighbors' horses, mend the plows, the axes and the broken hoes. He learned to sharpen tomahawks and fix the broken hammer of a musket, and this knowledge pleased the hotbloods and the hunters, especially those from the far towns.

Sometimes he picked up the die he had made with the name which Charley Hicks had written chiseled in the iron. With this die he had planned to mark his best silverwork. There were few enough opportunities now to use it.

For one thing the work at the great forge made it more difficult for his hands to manage the finer tools and he was often too tired to think of new designs. Shoeing horses was not easy for one who had to be careful of a lame leg. The knee of that leg sometimes had a way of swelling painfully. When this happened he discovered that the whiskey brought relief.

Occasionally a whiteman who came with work of some sort

had to wake him. Then the unwelcome customer ordered him about as though he were a slave. The roadbuilding was going faster now — the white settlements on one side of the Overhills would shortly be linked with the white settlements farther west. The whitemen were glad enough to have the blacksmith's services.

"When the roads are finished you will have more work," one whiteman told him. "You can buy more whiskey." The speaker laughed; that laugh was not a good thing to hear.

The Lame One bent over the hoof he was shaving and thought how tightly the smothering blanket of whitemen was being drawn about the Cherokees. As he nailed the shoe the hammer kept time to his thoughts. He had learned to be a blacksmith to serve his own people, not to aid these intruders among them, nor to keep their horses shod for the new roads they were constantly building.

The whiteman never knew, but before the Cherokee smith had finished his task, his mind was made up. He too would go away, to one of the far towns.

There was no longer any reason why he should not. Since he had become a silversmith the seasons had passed swiftly. The children were already grown and had their own cabins. U-ti-yu was ill, but that he believed was a passing matter. He had given her the proper plant brews to cure her illness.

He was sick and tired of the whitemen, tired of Indians who imitated them, tired of the sight of their ugly trousers and uglier hats, of plows and looms and spinning wheels, tired of hives of whiteman's bees set by Indian cabins, and of satisfied purring cats, who looked at him out of slanted eyes.

And then, suddenly, U-ti-yu was gone. He had not found the right plant for her after all. With the cabin empty the Lame One realized how lonely he was and how much he hated the whites. Nothing seemed as worthwhile as the Indian life he had known in the old days.

Surely when he reached the far towns he would find life as it used to be when he was a boy. He should have gone there long ago, before the smothering blanket began drawing so tight about the Overhills. He remembered the old song of warning of the mother bear. And he felt once again as he had in his childhood that he was the prey and the hunters were close:

"Tsâ' gĭ, tsâ' gĭ, hwĭ'lahĭ;
Tsâ' gĭ, tsâ' gĭ, hwĭ'lahĭ."

"I am going to Willstown," he said briefly, when others saw his preparations and asked him the question he had so often asked.

The listeners nodded, thinking of Doublehead and of Old Tassel's nephews. The Lame One did not explain that he was going chiefly because Agi-li was there and he needed him. Surely together they would find the old days. He wondered now and then what sort of a man Agi-li was when not surrounded by the dignity of the council. He had heard he was a firm chieftain.

Agi-li had to be firm. This the Lame One discovered almost as soon as he reached Willstown. For that settlement near the Coosa held a curious mixture, those Cherokees who followed and believed in the old ways, in the old spells and the old magic; those who hated the whites and wanted to be far from them; and those who were merely lazy and malcontent, wanting always to be where they were not, carrying discontent and anger as seeds within themselves; those lacking in wisdom and not really desiring it.

Agi-li was busied from morning until night, but this last group welcomed the Lame One heartily. They gathered like flies in the cabin he acquired and listened to his stories as long as the whiskey keg was opened. After a little the Lame One realized that they promptly forgot what he said and did not take a single word away with them. Yet because he was lonely the Lame One welcomed them. And he himself began drinking morc and more often from the keg.

The wilderness was close and the game still abundant. But the newcomer found that the life of the Cherokees in Willstown was not the same as it had been in his youth at Tuskegee. Not in Willstown, not in his cabin, nor on the trails was it the same. Only in his memory could he find the old days — in his memory and a jug of whiskey. He could not get along without the whiskey now. It was the only real friend he knew. It helped him to remember.

He would take a full jug in the morning and go out to the woods. There in the deepest shadows he could find, he would drink the whiskey slowly and sing the old songs, tell the old stories, not to any audience, only to himself. At times he felt as though he were living in the ancient days before he or his mother were born, in the days when the animals and the growing things and the Indians were friends — in the old, old days of Keetoowah.

Monotonously he would chant in a singsong fashion everything he had learned, songs and stories deep buried, but now falling easily from his lips as though he had heard them but yesterday. When the whiskey was gone and the stream of memory drained, he would lean back on the leaves and sleep a long time.

When he came to himself he would be nauseated. The forest was drab and uninviting. He would slink into town, avoiding anyone on the way. He would slip into his littered cabin and shut the door. He was greatly ashamed. The horse he had owned, his trade goods and his silverwork had all disappeared. Almost everything had been traded for kegs of whiskey, kegs which were empty, and had, when they were full, contained only illusion. Yet somehow or other, he would manage to obtain one more keg.

From this he would fill up the jug again and take his way almost joyfully to the woods.

He had thought once or twice of going to Agi-li and of telling him how it was with him. But he never did. He thought constantly however of the Chieftain of Willstown.

And then one day as he sat on a mossy bank, chanting mournfully of the past, the bushes in front of him parted and Agi-li stood there. The singing one did not pause, for he saw things as he chanted and he thought this was part of the vision.

The Lame One looked happily at Agi-li, anticipating his smile. Then his heart sank. For on Agi-li's face was a mixture of disgust and fury.

Yet when he spoke his voice was low and controlled, so low that Wurteh's son sat up and leaned forward to listen. But when the words, which the Chieftain of Willstown uttered, pierced through the past with which the Lame One had surrounded himself, when they woke his dulled comprehension into consciousness, they stung like so many arrows, each drilled to a sharp point and tipped with venom:

"How dare you sing of the past and of the great days of the Cherokee People? You, who drink the white man's liquor until you are nothing but a worthless sot! It is you and others like you, who have destroyed those days that are gone, and drowned the wisdom of the past forever.

"Two evils the whiteman gave us, and that I have heard in a single year — the smallpox in the ships, which brought likewise their black slaves, and their whiskey. They sent the pox and the whiskey among us to destroy us. And the pox killed half our people in a single season. Yet the whiskey was the greater evil. For it has destroyed the souls of the Cherokees.

"You sing of old spells and I know those spells. I learned them with you when we were boys, and from the same medicine men, the identical storytellers. I have seen the time such things were powerful. They are so no longer. For little by little the Indian has been caught in the power of this whiskey, until at last he cannot free himself.

"He is no good to himself, and that does not matter so much. He is no good to his family, and that matters some. But he is no good to the Cherokee Nation either. And that matters a great deal.

"In the old days the Cherokees served one another. Keetoowah, the clan of the priests, kept the wisdom and the strength of all the clans. The Keetoowah worked all the time for the tribe.

"Then the Keetoowah was gone, and the wise men, the leaders such as Old Tassel did much to take their place.

"But who thinks of the tribe, the clans, or of priestly matters now? Each man thinks only of himself. This too is what we have learned from the whitemen. Even Doublehead — "

Agi-li stopped suddenly as though he realized he was saying too much. The Lame One was thankful enough that the words had ceased. He blinked his bleary eyes and tried to steady his sagging mouth. He felt the saliva running down his chin, but his shaking hand could not seem to find the proper place to wipe it away.

Then Agi-li was speaking once again. He was his friend, his cousin no longer. He was a stranger, a chieftain who must consider the crime and pronounce the verdict.

The Lame One shivered, for he was not yet entirely free from the world into which he was passing when Agi-li had arrived. Would he be burned at the stake, he wondered, or hacked in pieces and given to the forest creatures, to the birds and the snakes? Would he —? His ears compelled him to listen:

"I have thought much about you since you came to Willstown. And I have been grieved at what I have heard and seen. I came more than once to your cabin, hoping to help you, to recall you to yourself. But you were surrounded with those of little account and I did not enter. Now I am too late.

"Yesterday you were a man in his prime, but the whiskey has made you old and useless. My talk I see is a waste of words. Nothing can be done. Once I had hoped great things from you. I believed you were not as so many have proved themselves to be. But now — You cannot escape from the evil. It is a rattlesnake wound tightly about you. You cannot — "

Cannot! He, the Lame One! Cannot!

Wurteh's son was struggling to his feet. His head swung from side to side and his footing was uncertain, his legs like reeds shaking in a wind. He slipped and would have fallen prone had he not grabbed a sapling and somehow managed to hold himself erect. He twisted his knee as he did so, the knee of the shortened leg. He scarcely felt the pain, though it sobered him. He held fast to the sapling and for an instant his shoulders were straight.

He raised the other hand that held the half-emptied jug and

threw it in a low curve into the bushes. There was a crash as it struck a rock, and a brief gurgle. He tried to speak, but his mouth would not obey him.

Agi-li — George Lowry — had turned away. What use, the shrug of his shoulders said, to talk to a drunken man?

No use at all. But still — In a broken voice, as though Agi-li was grieved almost beyond speaking, came his final plea.

"I had thought your knowledge, your memory, would be of great help to our people. I have memories of the old days when we spoke together of such things. I had counted on them — and on you."

The Lame One heard Agi-li's voice quiver, Agi-li his friend of old! He held fast to the sapling, for he felt as though he must fall — not from the effects of the whiskey this time, nor of the knives at his knee, but from the hurt in Agi-li's words.

Without a backward look the speaker walked away. Again and again the other tried to call after him. But the Lame One's tongue was too thick to obey him. He uttered no intelligible sound.

When Agi-li had disappeared, the Lame One sank in a huddled heap on the ground. He lay there for a long time.

At last he woke. As he went home a mixture of thoughts filled his head like so many gnats buzzing over a damp pool. Agi-li had broken the spell which the whiteman's whiskey had put upon him, and that spell had been great indeed. But, the whirling thoughts insisted, if the whiteman had such powers to destroy, what about his other powers — those which built and conquered? Such were the powers, the magic, with which the intruding folk had made themselves strong. Once he had thought much about these matters, and had wondered how such powers could be used by the Cherokees. The talking leaves, for instance.

Talking leaves.

He had almost forgotten.

VI

That Which Eyes Cannot Learn

(About 1810–1813)

IT IS A strange thing to change the course of one's life. It is like damming a river and making it flow in another direction. The Lame One lay on his bed and considered what he should do with the new man he had become.

And like a picture painted on deerskin, like a design on a wampum belt, came that ever-haunting memory of the night on the Wabash. He could almost hear the crackle of the bark clutched in his fingers. That night he had been certain the talking leaves held the answer — the answer for the tribe.

He lay still and left his mind open to wisdom, as the Keetoowah, the priestly ones, had done, according to what the old men had often told him. After a time he understood that the vision of that night had returned again and again because it was true. He could not have told anyone how he knew. But he did. It was the old god-knowledge of the Ani-Keetoowah, the priestly clan of the Principal People — the clan that was no more.

Then — in the old days, the priests had fasted and prayed long for answers to the problems of the Nation. And when the answers came the priests too had been certain.

There was a little click on the roof, and outside a boy began singing:

"Da'yi, skinta; Da'yi skinta."
(Beaver, put a tooth into my jaw,
Beaver, put a tooth into my jaw.)

That likewise was old wisdom. The youngster was certain of the answer, certain that he would soon have a new and sturdy tooth in place of this one he had thrown over the Lame One's roof.

The boy had begun the line for the fourth time, when suddenly the singing changed into a shriek, a shriek such as a coward might make when the Creeks in full war regalia sprang from a hiding place. It was followed by another and another. When the Lame One reached the door the boy was clinging to his mother, shuddering and hiding his head desperately in her calico dress.

Then out of the woods came a whiteman, one of those wandering souls, whom his own kind deemed crazy, but who the Indians understood was decoyed into the forest by the Little People, who live in hollow trees and on rocky cliffs. This man desired, as the Lame One knew, neither land nor possessions, but only to wander as it pleased him, and as the needs of the weather drove.

The boy who had shrieked with dismay and fear, his mother explained, had never seen a whiteman before. He had however heard all the tales, which she and others at Willstown had told him, of what whitemen had done to the Cherokees in the days when she was young.

With a feeling of disgust the Lame One slammed the door. The storytellers here talked too much of matters which were not important. They had not spoken often enough of such things as became a Cherokee. This boy had need of tales of Cherokee courage even in the face of torture and death. Then he would run screaming from no man. The pride of his race would keep him strong.

Once *he* could have told such stories in a way that Cherokee boys would listen and would remember. But now apparently he had lost the knack of telling them in the proper fashion. Besides, it would be, he felt, like pouring meal through a corn-sifter. He must learn how to put down what he knew, even as he had once planned, on the talking leaves.

There was only one way to go about it. That was the way he had learned the secrets of the medicine men, of the hunter and trader, the secrets both of the silversmiths and the black-smiths. He must use his eyes and his ears. He must go and watch and listen at the door of the whitemen's school, which the chieftains had permitted on Cherokee land. Thus he would learn easily enough how it was the whitemen put their talk on paper. Then he would come home and do the same thing for the Cherokees — only perhaps he would do it better!

The Lame One had an influence over others when he was not drinking. The old men said it was because he belonged to the Red Paint Clan, and all Cherokees knew that mighty conjurers came from this clan. So he found it easy enough to borrow a horse from a man he had scarcely seen before. And without saying where he was going, he rode off.

About fifteen miles from Oostanaula — where the new council fire burned, and where Charley Hicks now lived — and on the trail which led on into the Overhill Towns was a school. This was the one which the chieftains at Tellico had considered, and of which Charley Hicks had told him the day Charley had written down his name. Here the whitemen were teaching Cherokee children the things which white children learned — how to put talk on paper, and how to say that talk aloud, even as in the old days the Cherokee young men had been taught word for word what the wampum belts meant.

It was a long ride and the man took his time. Wrapped in cloth and tied behind him on his saddle were three small cakes of corn and beans. There were places along the trail which reminded him of ambushes Doublehead had made upon the whites; there were towns where Doublehead had hung up white scalps and incited the young men to join him to have revenge for Old Tassel's death. The murder of the Beloved Man had cost the white settlers many a scalp.

Old Tassel, that Beloved One, had never told a lie! But Doublehead! The Lame One knew now to what Agi-li was referring when he called out the name of Doublehead in anger.

Better might his name have been Doubletongue, for he had betrayed his people. His prestige which came from his fame as a warrior, his strong voice at the council fire had served as his downfall. For finally, Doublehead, who had long trafficked with the Spanish in Florida for ammunition and guns to kill the Americans, had gone to the council fire of the Great White Father. From there he had come back loaded with gifts for the tribe, the greater part of which he kept for himself. After that whiskey and bribery led fast to Doublehead's treachery. With no authority from the Cherokee council he had ceded Indian land near the Overhills, the land north and west of the Tennessee, the best hunting ground of the tribe. He had forgotten the old ways and worked not for the good of the tribe but to gain possessions for himself. *Unaga! Whiteman!*

When a tribesman betrayed his people, he became an outlaw meriting death. Especially was this so if he disposed of land without the council's authority. These matters Doublehead understood full well.

The Lame One did not know exactly how it had come about, but it was thought the council had ordered Gunun′da le′gi — He-Who-Walks-on-the-Ridge — to kill the traitor. At any rate after the deed was done Gunun′da le′gi spoke up in the council and declared that the Cherokees must stand together as one. For that reason it was decided that the old law of clan revenge would be set at naught. Even Doublehead's closest relatives must not avenge his death. It was a good thing for the tribe that Doublehead had been killed. That was clear. And it was a wise law too that in the future no Cherokees should seek revenge for a kinsman's death. The tribe was too small now for such killings.

The relatives of Doublehead accepted the new law. But Bird, his son, would go out of his way in order not to meet his father's slayer, He-Who-Walks-on-the-Ridge. The Ridge was warned to beware of Bird.

The Lame One shook his head. Enough of such thinking. He must empty his mind and keep it thus, empty and tranquil, ready for the new knowledge he was about to acquire. When he returned from the whiteman's school it would be different. He would have much to think about!

The horse knew the trail and the rider did not even have to guide him. Perhaps it was just as well. For though he passed others and met several, the Lame One spoke to none. More than once a rider reined in to look curiously after him, recalling as he did so, some conjurer deeply intent upon strange spells.

When at length the Lame One came to that part of the trail not far from Sumac Town and Rabbit Trap, he reined in his horse and sat quietly for a long time, as though loath to take the final step toward knowledge. Only when his vision was strong once more did he go on.

He came to a spot overlooking Springplace, and left his horse tethered where there was plenty of grass. From there the Lame One went forward on foot. Here there were cabins and a large barn set among shade trees, an orchard of apple, cherry and peach. His ears were already serving him, for he went straight toward the cabin where he heard talk in the whiteman's language.

He opened the door and moved forward with no sound of his moccasined feet. A glance past the shoulder of the nearest boy was enough, and the Lame One reached over and removed the bundle of talking leaves from the seated one's hands. His eyes and his fingers were eager. He paid no attention to the tap-tap of shoes behind him.

But as quickly and as competently as he himself had done it, the book was snatched from his hands and restored to the boy. At the same time a second and smaller book was thrust toward him.

For once the Lame One was startled.

He whirled about and stared down into the eyes of a pleasant-faced whitewoman. She was — in the fashion of the Moravians — wearing a little white cap on her head, tied with light blue ribbons underneath her chin. She was neatly dressed in brown, with a cloth as white as swan's feathers folded about her shoulders, and another tied at her waist. Her face was gentle, though for a moment the Lame One had caught a glimpse of sparks in her eyes.

She spoke, but the Lame One could not understand. He had refused to learn English words, had closed his ears to the sound of them, had made his mind empty of memory. So now in Cherokee he explained briefly what he wanted.

At once the expression on the woman's face grew gentle, for

the Lame One's voice was soft and musical. For a moment the Lame One thought she understood. She turned and said something to a second white person in the room. This was a man who had been guiding the hand of one of the pupils. The man came forward now and spoke.

The Lame One could not understand his words any more than he had those of the woman. So he began using the language of signs. He held up the talking leaf bundle which the woman had handed him. He pointed to the children and to himself.

The man and woman waited.

The pupil who had been writing laid aside his quill pen. The Lame One, remembering Charley Hicks, picked it up and touched it to the bundle of talking leaves which the woman had handed him. But the woman shook her head and removed the pen before its tip should stain the page.

Suddenly Wurteh's son thought of the bracelet he wore — the only bit of his silverwork remaining. He took it off and pointed to the name which his die had made upon it.

"George Guess," read the man. "I am Brother Gambold and this is my wife." He extended his hand which the Cherokee took politely. "We are glad you have come."

It was the Lame One's turn to be pleased at the reading of his name, the tone of the greeting. He held out the bracelet for the woman to see. And she echoed the name.

The Cherokee repeated his errand once more in his own language.

The man turned helplessly toward the pupils. One of them was already on his feet, eager to explain. "He says he has come to find out how you make talk on leaves."

"Oh!" The whiteman spoke to the boy, who interpreted this time in Cherokee. "He says to sit down with the others and he will show you."

The children giggled as the Lame One took his place beside them.

The woman slipped from the room, but the man seated himself beside the Lame One and showed him a picture that looked like a horse's shoe. "C," he said. "A," he added as he showed him a picture of a wigwam with a log stretched across it. "T," he said, and he showed a picture of a tree with drooping limbs. "Cat," he ended triumphantly.

"Wesa," translated the boy on the Lame One's other side.

But that is whiteman's language, thought the Lame One, dismayed and irritated at the turn the teaching had taken. He had not come to learn of whiteman's cats, nor of other white ways, only of the way they put down their talk and kept it forever.

"Do it in Cherokee talk," he demanded.

The boy translated.

The man shook his head. "If we only could."

Though the Lame One had not understood the words, he knew the meaning of what the man had said even before the boy explained.

The whiteman too was a watcher of faces. He had to be. He was now attempting — without much success — to learn

Cherokee. The lack of a written language was a great handicap.

The missionary explained this, and added: "Tell our visitor, George Guess, that it can be done. Indian talk can be set down on paper. But an Indian, I think, will have to do it. It is difficult because Cherokees do not speak as we do. We have no sounds in our language for some which are in the Indian tongue. But surely, it can be done. It will be done in time. Charley Hicks has tried, but he says he cannot do it. Tell this man that perhaps he will be the one who can."

The whiteman could see that a great desire had drawn the Indian into the schoolroom. He must do what he could to satisfy that desire. Who knew where the seed might fall, or when a miracle might be accomplished?

Again he drew the picture of the wigwam. "A," he said. He drew a picture of two horseshoes placed side by side. "B." And a single, large shoe, "C." A bow with a string was "D." He went on until he had the piece of paper filled with pictures. The Lame One noticed how he uttered a single sound and a different one for each picture he drew.

For an instant comprehension was on the Indian's face — a different picture and a different sound — a single sound.

And then once again, the man put three pictures side by side, and said as before, "Cat!"

That was a single sound too. And yet there were *three* pictures! It was most confusing. And why did he always bring in that evil creature — the cat?

The glimmer of understanding had gone now. The whiteman was choosing from the books on the table. He placed one in the Cherokee's hands, while the boy interpreted. "He says to tell you it is a spelling book, and that all the letters for making talk are on the first page." There being no Indian word for letters or spelling, the boy used the whiteman's words for them. "He is giving the book to you."

The Cherokee remained the rest of the day, but he did not learn any more about the talking leaves. He watched the children go to their meal, he watched them working in the cornfield and painting a fence. He wandered in a garden which was different from any he had seen about whitemen's houses, for this had plants such as grew in the forest, on the mountains, in the swamps. Many of them were those which the medicine men searched for, and their uses he knew. It was plain that these white people realized they were good plants to have. The woman in the white bonnet with its bright ribbons tied at her chin came out to work in the garden. He knew from the way she moved about, the way she patted the ground, and even spoke to the plants — that it was her garden.

He ate his last cake of corn and beans. He drank from a spring.

He heard the sound of a hammer and went toward the mission's blacksmith shop. There a whiteman was helping an Indian build a wagon. The Lame One thought that if one wagon was built, there would soon be others. Then there would be wagon roads. And this even though the chieftains had refused their permission, declaring that they saw no need of roads through the Cherokee land. As it was, the whitemen had no trouble in finding their way along the Indian trails. But the road matter, no doubt, would be like the cessions of land, in the end the whites would have their road, until — Until what? If he would help his people, he must not delay.

He turned away from the group of buildings and went back to the borrowed horse. As he set out for Willstown his thoughts were like a wind which blows from all directions. Every now and then he would pause and finger the bundle of talking leaves. He looked again and again at the page where the boy had pointed out all the letters for making talk! *Letters* meant pictures — So much was clear. The Lame One found the pictures the whiteman had drawn on paper and slipped inside the book. He saw where the whiteman had put three pictures together and had said "Cat." He felt utterly bewildered.

Still he had gained one thing, the assurance that Cherokee talk could be set down even as the whiteman's. And the whiteman had said that an Indian must do it.

He was the one who was to accomplish the task. This he had sensed for a long time. Yet it was something not to be learned with eyes. This was knowledge deep hidden, which must be traced through the thickets of his thoughts, as a river is traced, slowly, bend by bend. This was something to be done alone!

He reached Willstown at last and got down from the horse. The creature released went home to his master. It was well, for the man had forgotten that the horse had been borrowed. He had forgotten that he was hungry. He sat in the doorway of his cabin until it was quite dark, looking at the bundle of talking leaves he had brought.

In the morning he sat there again, looking at the book and making the pictures, such as the man had made, with a stick on the ground. He did not remember the sounds but he made the pictures. As he had done on the Wabash he found a stone that would mark on another and made the pictures on the stone.

The rain washed out the marks on the ground and stones such as he needed were not always available. Then he found that he could cut the pictures with his knife out of bark. He found trees which were most suitable and did this. The cabin floor was littered with the results of his work.

The Lame One did not go into the woods with a keg of whiskey any more. But neither did he mix with the others. The days passed, new moons came and went, the seasons changed. The Lame One's cabin was untended and he did not do his share of work in the fields about Willstown, though he took what he needed from the community store. He grew gaunt and thin and his eyes were tired and had a strained look.

If anyone came asking him to fix a gun lock, a broken tomahawk or a shovel, he would wave them aside.

"Do not trouble me, I am busy."

"Busy?"

The people questioned one another. "Busy — at what?"

There were some old men in the town who had an answer to

this question. But when Agi-li heard what they were saying, he ordered them to be quiet.

After that they said what they had to say in whispers. Whispers such as theirs make a louder noise than words. Agi-li realized that something must be done.

VII

A Cherokee and His Duty

(Autumn 1813)

THE CHICADEE, the tsi′kilili′ had been singing all the morning on a branch of a tree outside the Lame One's door. The song had penetrated even to the Lame One. For when the tsi′kilili′ sings thus one of two things is certain, either someone you know is returning from a journey, or evil is being plotted against you.

Surely no one had reason to plot against him. Perhaps Agi-li had been away and was returning. He would like to see him, if this matter of the talking leaves did not keep him so busied. And so weary. Yesterday when he went for more tree bark he had found an owl's feather, and he soaked this for a long time in water and washed his eyes with it. But still he had fallen asleep over his work. He was very tired. If only he wasn't so tired and could think more clearly, he would be able to trap the secret of the talking leaves.

Almost in response to his thoughts, as it were, Agi-li was at his door. The Lame One was glad to see him, even though Agi-li appeared a little confused and at a loss as to what to say after he had greeted the Lame One.

Still it was clear to Wurteh's son that the Chieftain had come for a purpose. So he waited for him to speak.

Agi-li looked about the littered cabin. He looked at the Lame One.

"The old men are making much talk," he said at last. "That is why I have come. The difficulties for the Cherokee People are growing greater, and the old men say it is because you, like Doublehead, are working against them."

"I! Like Doublehead!"

The astonishment of the Lame One was complete. Even Agi-li, who in spite of himself had been a trifle swayed by the old ones, was convinced for a moment.

Half apologetically he went on: "They recall that Wurteh was of the Red Paint Clan and from that clan have come our greatest conjurers. They remember you have been much with the medicine men. And they declare you are fashioning new and strange spells. These spells are bringing disaster to the Cherokee People."

"Wait!" said the Lame One, holding up his hand. "What was it that you said?"

Agi-li repeated.

The Lame One nodded. "Good! You spoke a word then I had forgotten entirely. I will make a picture of it — so." He began cutting the bark in his hand. "I am making pictures of every word I can think of — a new picture for each word. I am trying to remember them all."

But Agi-li reached out and took the bark and knife from the Lame One's fingers. Once more he began speaking. He kept his voice as calm and low as he could. For he did not like the look on the Lame One's face. It was clear that something must be done at once to take this man away from the solitude in which he had remained so long.

"I have come," he said, "to ask you to leave this child's play and go with me to the council at Oostanaula."

The Lame One started to interrupt, but Agi-li held up his hand for silence.

"I have told you before that each man must work not for himself but for the Nation. Of what use are you to the Nation when you sit here with your mumbling? If you were ill the people would not mind caring for you. But you are not ill."

"I am making wings for the Ground Squirrel," declared the Lame One, "so that he can play on the side of the Cherokees."

At the words a look of dismay went over Agi-li's face. Turtle Fields had said that the Lame One was making a fool of himself. But making a fool of one's self was a better thing than the fashioning of evil spells. Agi-li put his words cautiously now, and more diplomatically. "You will not be respected if you continue longer with this."

The dreaming look had gone from the Lame One's eyes. His words were curt: "If I am no longer respected, what I am doing will not make our people less respected. Tell them I shall continue."

But Agi-li pretended not to have heard. "Your roof leaks and the wind plays through the chinks between the logs. For a long time you have not been seen going to the water to bathe at the rising of the new moon, nor at the time of the eating of the new corn. Even those who have become most like the white-man do not omit the rites of the festival of the new corn, nor the rites of the new fire. You no longer give heed to these matters. Instead you sit here and play with trash like a small one unable to walk."

Agi-li paused. He had not meant to say that about walking. Yet it had come to his lips easily enough because of the suggestions of the old men. They were afraid of what the son of Wurteh was doing, largely because he was lame.

Agi-li had told them the idea was foolish, that Old Hop, one of the greatest of the Cherokee chieftains at Echota in the days of its glory, had been lame. And so was Charley Hicks, for that matter.

The old men had an answer for that. "The wise men told us when we were young that a cripple has great powers for good or for evil. Because of this the medicine men used the bark of the crippled tree with care, and some would not use it at all."

They said: "Of Old Hop or of Charley Hicks we are not speaking. These have worked for the good of the tribe. But now the days grow darker, the danger to the tribe greater, the talk of sending us away from our homes is increasing. All this has come about, we have observed, since the Lame One began his queer mumbling, his work with strange spells. In the dark some of us have hidden close to his house and we have heard him say word after word aloud, but there was no sense in what he was saying — not to us. To him there was sense. He has always known the old wisdom. Now he has gone further than anyone has gone, and he knows more. He is bewitched and he is bewitching the Nation."

Agi-li wished for a second time that he had not said that about a child unable to walk. He knew full well how sensitive the Lame One had always been about his shortened leg, and how in spite of it he had participated in whatever the others did. Agi-li recalled the set look on the Lame One's face, when as a boy he came in the last at the races. With a sudden inspiration the Chieftain of Willstown hurried on.

"There is a way for you to redeem yourself. We are, I think, about to make war with the Americans on the Creeks. And I want you to come with us."

The Lame One stared. Agi-li had said he was acting like a child unable to walk. And in the next breath he asked him to go to war against the Creeks. He was wanted with the warriors, he, the Lame One.

"Will the warriors permit it?"

"I am the Chieftain of Willstown. I can tell of the days when we were both young. In those days you were a good hunter and had many brave deeds to your credit. And did you not go to the Wabash with the Badger?"

The other nodded.

Better, thought Agi-li to himself, to take the Lame One from his spell-making, even though he died on the journey. He was probably harmless, injuring as he claimed no one but himself. Still, there were the strange words about making wings for the ground squirrel. For some reason the words seemed familiar, and yet Agi-li could not place them.

There was something else which puzzled and frightened him, and that was the curious dignity about the man. He had seen such dignity among conjurers sure of their knowledge and power.

Agi-li was shaking his head as he left. He wanted to forget what the old men had said. He wanted to deny his own thoughts.

Behind him the Lame One began stacking his pieces of bark in neat piles. He had promised to go to the council and there was much to do. It was a long time since he had been any distance at all from his cabin.

Yet even when the time came and he went with Agi-li to Oostanaula, it seemed as though a part of him remained behind in the cabin with his precious pieces of bark. It was a difficult task to which he had set himself. At times it seemed impossible. How could he make a picture for every different word? How could he remember them all?

Someone nudged him. The pipe was waiting. He puffed it and passed it on. He glimpsed briefly, through the haze of smoke and his thoughts, Charley Hicks seated beside Pathkiller, now the Principal Chieftain. Then he was back again with his word pictures, not bothered by the medicine dance nor the low thrum, thrumming of the drums. He came fully to the council fire only when a Cherokee from Coo'sawatee began speaking. The speaker declared he was a prophet from the mountains, and was sent by a prophet from another mighty tribe, the Shawnees. The Shawnee prophet was Tecumseh, the Shooting Star. This leader, with the help of the Indians' gods and the Indians themselves, to say nothing of the White Father across the seas, the English King, had promised to give back all the country as it was of old to the Indians. Englishmen and Americans, it seemed, were once again on the warpath. The prophet's voice sharpened, his eyes shone:

"The English believe in Tecumseh and have made him a general. The Creeks, those mighty warriors, have listened to his words and have sent forth the bundles of red sticks. One stick a day is broken, and when the last is in two pieces the Creeks, who are friends of the English, will make war on the Americans. Red Eagle is leading the Creek Warriors — the Red Sticks. They ask us as their brothers, to join with them, to take up the war hatchet and sound the war cry.

"Like the Creeks, we Cherokees should dance the new dance against the whitemen, the dance of the lakes, for it is powerful medicine. Even now the old magic of the Indians has begun working. There is a new star in the heavens with a tail streaming behind it. That is Tecumseh's star. Tecumseh has only to stamp his foot and the whole earth trembles. Stones will fall from the skies, when we set forth together, upon our enemies.

"I am a prophet who has been sent to tell you these things. Some of our people will not receive what I have to tell. But still I must tell it. Let the tribes but join together!"

The Lame One was listening intently now. This was the same sort of talk he had heard as a young man when he had gone north to the Wabash. Then the Indians had allied with the English and had indeed won a victory over the borderers. But that victory had been like snow, so quickly had its effects disappeared. Now out of the north, another had come who preached the same thing — that the tribes joining together could drive out the whiteman. Yet the tribes were fewer and the numbers of each were smaller, while the numbers of the Americans had multiplied beyond the counting.

"We, the Cherokees, are a great people. For us was laid out a straight road since the beginning. We ourselves have broken the road which was given to our fathers. We have taken the clothes and the worthless trinkets of the whitemen. We have put beds and tables in our houses, and set up mills in our towns, while the cats prowl from cabin to cabin and are fed and even stroked by Cherokee hands.

"All these things are bad. We, the Indians, should live as our fathers before us lived. We should not think of our tribe only but of all the Indian nations. In this way we can grow strong. In this way we can be at peace with ourselves as we were in the old days. If we would seek this peace, let us put off the whiteman's dress forever. Let us put on paint and buckskin. Let us throw away all the things which the whitemen has brought, his plows, his spinning wheels and the weaving looms. And let us kill the cats! Only if we are Indians again and think and fight in the old way can victory be ours. Otherwise the Indian will disappear forever. It is like this:"

The prophet from Coo'sawatee lifted a club in his clenched fist. Dramatically he removed one finger and then another, until the club fell with a thud to the earthen floor.

"The clenched fist is the Indian tribes working together. The loosening of the fingers is the separating of the tribes, one from another. That is how the whitemen tricked us — into making us loosen our fingers. Let us loosen them no longer. Let us close them tight and defy the Americans!"

A roar of approval went up in the council house. In that roar the Lame One sensed all the bewilderment, the suppressed fury and sadness of a generation. It held terror too and promise of vengeance.

Through that sound a man moved to take his place where the prophet from Coo'sawatee had been standing. This was a full-blood, the Lame One judged, but to him a stranger. He was tall and powerful of frame. His thick hair rose like a turban of feathers from his forehead, his eyes were dark and commanding. The Lame One saw Charley Hicks speak to the Pathkiller. The Chieftain nodded. He was recognizing the new man, was permitting him to speak.

"Who?" whispered the Lame One to his neighbor. For he sensed by the tall man's deliberate movements, and the way he waited for the circle about him to become quiet again, that here was a leader certain of himself. There was a feeling too that this was someone he should know. For the first time he realized how long a time he had spent with his bark pictures.

"He-Who-Walks-on-the-Ridge," said his neighbor. "From Ookellogee Valley." Another shortened the name to "The Ridge."

The Lame One nodded. The killer of Doublehead! He who had dared all of Doublehead's clan, and all of Doublehead's followers. Yet no one had touched him. He was a brave man. He had not known how his deed would be judged. It was something which the council believed should be done for the good of the Principal People. So he had killed the traitor — the one who had sold the Cherokee People's land.

The new man spoke slowly and with great calm. The Lame One however noticed that his eyes swept over the audience as though he were indeed walking on a ridge, a narrow ridge with deep abysses on either side. Yet his feet were certain. His tongue did not falter.

The Lame One's heart leaped at the first words.

"Already I have noticed that there are men here who have remembered talks such as this we have just heard. They can tell you better than I what happened when the tribes moved together against the whitemen in the old days. That was when I lived on the Hiwassee. The Americans came then and burned our homes again and again and killed our people. I have killed whitemen for what was done then. I have chased the buffalo through the dark and bloody ground, where no buffalo roam now. And I have taken my family away from the whitemen so that we live in the wilderness."

For an instant it seemed as though the man's eyes lingered on those of the Lame One. Then he went on and the words were dark. Yet the Lame One knew he spoke truth, and one must recognize truth even when it is displeasing.

"Yet I say that what has been told you is crooked talk. The days of resisting the whitemen are past. I say this as a Cherokee, a believer in the Principal People. We must learn another way than that of resistance. If we have time and space we can learn it. If not, we are forever lost.

"Look about you and see with your own eyes. The whitemen have come in on the north. What was our land is ours no longer. It is the whiteman's Tennessee. Some of you yet live in the mountains of our grandfathers. But the whitemen name the land Carolina.* We hold our council fire on what we still call our land. But the whitemen declare it is part of their Georgia. For some years the whiteman has been urging that we have no right at all to the land which was ours before the whiteman came, that we should move beyond the Mississippi. What the end will be, we do not know.

"This however we do know. We are a people who have been great. We can be great again. But we cannot find the trail to greatness through warring against the Americans. If we do that we find only the trail to our own destruction. The Creeks are taking that trail. For us there must be another way.

* In 1816, by treaty, the Cherokees gave up all their land in South Carolina.

"Now, for our own preservation, we must move with and not against the Americans. I, a Cherokee, say we must fight our old enemies the Creeks, at the side of the Americans!"

The muttering in the crowd had grown louder as the speaker continued. When he ended, for a second time that night there was a roar. This time it sounded like the roar of an enraged mountain lion at the throat of its prey.

Charley Hicks was on his feet. Pathkiller remained seated. But his voice and gestures were trying to calm the crowd. The bloodthirsty Cherokees gave no heed. They were surging upon The Ridge.

The Lame One could see the speaker no longer. His head with its bushy hair went down before the storm. Then the Lame One found himself fighting his way through the crowd to where he had last seen The Ridge. At his side was Agi-li and Charley Hicks. And other of the older and calmer men.

The Ridge lay motionless and trampled upon. Blood flowed from the wound where a knife had stabbed him. But from his place Pathkiller was restoring order. In the end he had it. In great quietness the wounded one was carried forth. The Lame One was among those sharing the burden.

After The Ridge had been taken into a friendly cabin for care, the Lame One did not return to the council. He walked back and forth under the stars, thinking of what had happened that night. Agi-li was right. He had stayed by himself too long. Before he was able to aid his people, the danger was upon them.

The talk of The Ridge had been wise talk. The solution did

not lie in fighting against the whitemen. The Cherokees must not be used again for the selfish purposes of the English King across the seas.

It seemed to him but yesterday when his life had changed sharply. Tonight he knew it had changed again. Tomorrow he would go with the warriors.

VIII

The Battle of Horseshoe Bend
(October 1813–March 1814)

FOR THREE summers and three winters the Lame One had been apart from his kind. He had thought only of words and of the pictures he made of them. Now he looked upon men and took a keen delight in what he saw. He thought about them when he lay down for the night, how they looked, what they said or did, of the conversation he had heard.

First of all he watched and thought about Agi-li and Charley Hicks. Agi-li was sharing with Aganstata the command of the regiment of foot and mounted Cherokees. Like himself, these two had enlisted under their whitemen's names — George Lowry and Gideon Morgan. He was recorded as George Guess.

The Charley Hicks he had known seemed more remote than ever from him now. Charley had recently decided that he would follow the God of the whitefolk at Springplace. He declared he was no less a Cherokee for so doing, and that he was as proud as ever of his race. But the Lame One could not understand the decision. He prized too much the old knowledge of Keetoowah to need another way.

There were others equally puzzled. One remarked that the whiteman's Book had been read to him and that the words seemed good. Strange, he added, that the white people were no better, after having had such wisdom so long.

To which Charley could reply honestly enough that those who had come to Springplace did take the teachings of their God seriously. *Their* word could be trusted. They were allowed to use the Indians' land, but they never asked to have it for themselves. Perhaps missionaries were different from other whitemen.

Besides Charley Hicks and Agi-li there were two others among the warriors who were much in the Lame One's thoughts. One was The Ridge, recovered of his wound, his head and shoulders looming above the rest of the tribe. At his side constantly was a young man with blue eyes and light skin. His name was John Ross and it was quite evident he had but little Indian blood. It was equally clear that he was proud of being a Cherokee, and was well liked by his fellows, though no doubt the sponsorship of The Ridge had something to do with this.

In thinking of Ross the Lame One was reminded of Agi-li when Agi-li was young. He understood the reason for this feeling when he heard one of the men who had come with Ross extol the latter's strength and hardihood. Ross, he learned, had spent the winter before on a long journey down the rivers and across the Mississippi itself on a mission to those Cherokees — a considerable number by now — who had gone west to live. It was feared these distant ones might yield to the persuasions of some of Tecumseh's messengers. Young Ross, therefore, had been sent to warn them against taking up arms with Tecumseh's tribes.

It had been a difficult journey. Ross and his three men had spent sixty days upon the rivers in the dead of winter. The whites whom they had seen were afraid of them, believing they were warriors, while the Shawnees and other Indians along the route either thought they were whites, or rightly judged and attempted to thwart their purpose in going to the Western Cherokees.

Everything that could happen to the party had happened. As a final catastrophe the boat had been wrecked and all the baggage lost. Yet, up to their knees in mud and water much of the way, Ross had urged his companions on. Their ancestors had killed game for food and they could too. So they had covered at least two hundred miles in an unknown country in this fashion. And that in eight days! Ross might have blue eyes, but the warriors conceded he was true Cherokee!

The Lame One concluded that Ross was one who would always complete whatever he undertook, no matter what the cost. He noted too the striking similarity in the lift of his head with that of The Ridge.

There was almost gaiety in the Lame One's heart the night

when the eastern warriors were joined by the group of Cherokees from the west. For there was the booming voice, the giant form, the laughter of John Jolly. In the old days Jolly had lived on the Hiwassee not far from where Charley Hicks had lived. He had always been a hunter and had gone on a few years ago across the Mississippi. There game was plentiful, he declared, and would be so forever if the white hunters who sneaked in were not so wasteful. Sometimes they would throw away a thousandweight of meat for perhaps twenty pounds of tallow. The Osages who were there were not friendly to the newcomers. Still, Jolly boasted, the life was like that their fathers had known. After all the Cherokees had never been concerned about the proximity of enemies.

As Jolly spoke of his companions in the west, the Lame One was astonished to hear familiar name after familiar name. Many of them had been in Willstown when he arrived there first, or in the other far towns. He was reminded now of the days when he had watched his friends, one by one, leaving the Overhill Towns in order to be farther away from the whiteman. Until now he had not realized that the same thing had been happening over again.

"Tsă'gĭ, tsă'gĭ, hwĭ'lahĭ;
Tsă'gĭ, tsă'gĭ, hwĭ'lahĭ."

Others in the regiment were eager with questions, and their delight at Jolly's answers was similar to what one would have shown on receiving word from those in the Ghost Country.

"Do you hear? It is Yane'gwa, my brother, of whom he is speaking!" Or, "I know the Squirrel well! He is my son!"

If only, thought the Lame One, he had but tracked down the secret of the talking leaves, then . . . Resolutely he turned his thoughts away. He had promised to become a warrior. He must not think of his other task — not now. He would put his thoughts instead upon the men from Willstown going with him on the whiteman's warpath. For the most part these were unimportant Cherokees like himself. It was good to be with John Drew, Going Back and Archibald Campbell. The friendship with Campbell was a growing one.

On another night there were Creeks beside the Cherokees at the campfire. These friendly Creeks, as their comrades called them, were under William McIntosh, chieftain of some of the Lower Towns. They were going to war against their own tribesmen. McIntosh had recognized, as had The Ridge, that it was suicidal for the Creek Nation to stand now against the Americans.

One day the Lame One saw two whitemen whom he had not seen before. The first was Andrew Jackson, with whose white troops from Tennessee the Cherokees were allied. The white soldiers called their leader Old Hickory, declaring he was fashioned from that toughest of woods. Where the danger was greatest, there Old Hickory was determined to go. When the Cherokees observed this, they renamed him Pointed Arrow.

The second whiteman was a youngster and the Lame One first observed him riding with an arm across John Jolly's shoulder. It was easy enough to guess that this was the adopted son of John Jolly, of whom every Cherokee had heard. As a boy he had swum across the Hiwassee to spend much of his time with the Cherokees. He had gone through all the ceremonies and had been named Kaluna, the warrior. After that no Indian called him by his white name — Sam Houston. He might be white, declared Jolly, but his heart and his courage both were Cherokee. There would always be a place for Kaluna at Jolly's fireside.

The troops, whitemen and Indians, were moving south. There the Red Sticks, the warriors of the Creek Nation, had broken the last stick in the bundle sent them by Tecumseh, and had attacked Fort Mims on the east bank of the Alabama. They had killed every whiteman, woman and child they had found.

Now, gathered on holy soil, the Red Sticks waited the coming of the enemy. So pregnant was the very earth where they stood with the magic of the ancients that their conjurers declared no whiteman could even step foot on the ground and live. But, true to his name, Pointed Arrow moved straight toward that sacred ground.

The Creeks had a long record of successful warfare. To this the Cherokees could testify, though they held their own record higher. Besides the English, behind the Creeks and urging them on, were the Spaniards in Florida. From the Spaniards came their arms and ammunition. The leader of the hostile Creeks was a mixed-blood. Weatherford was his white name;

his Creek one, Red Eagle. All these reports the Lame One heard from the Cherokee scouts.

Andrew Jackson — the Pointed Arrow — was both fearless and methodical. He destroyed one of the Creeks' main towns in November. Five days later he burned another. He entered and overcame the Red Sticks on their holiest ground, and not all the spells of their medicine men could stop him. Not then.

But the medicine men worked harder and said more and direful formulas. At last the tide turned.

The Cherokees knew one of the reasons. Many of the white-men under Jackson had volunteered for short terms only. When their time was up, they mutinied and the Pointed Arrow was hard put to hold them. So, when the Red Sticks attacked at Emuckfaw Creek, the Pointed Arrow was forced to withdraw. Again the Red Sticks struck and Andrew Jackson moved away faster with his men. The Creeks were derisive. They had turned the Pointed Arrow back across the Coosa. An arrow which could be bent back on itself was quite useless!

The Cherokees chafed under the Creeks' derision. When Jackson finally gave orders to move forward again, the Indian allies were determined that the Creeks should not associate them with another withdrawal.

As for the Red Sticks, they had won plenty of time to make ready for the attack which they knew must come. They had fortified themselves on a peninsula where the Tallapoosa swept around behind them in a great bend. Like a shining horseshoe, thought the Lame One, when he first saw it. That was the

Creeks' name for it — Horseshoe Bend. His glance moved appreciatively over the preparations which the Red Sticks had made.

At the neck of the peninsula the Creeks had fashioned a cypress-log breastwork, jutting back and forth — like the white-men's rail fences. The peninsula itself was furrowed with gullies and covered with timber and bushes and in its midst was a Creek town. At the rear, where the waters of the horseshoe made the bend, a fleet of canoes was tied. Should the Red Sticks be forced back toward that point, they had a means for escaping.

But Cherokee scouts had their orders. Far up the river bank, out of sight of the enemy, they were swimming across the Tallapoosa, or moving in dugouts hastily fashioned. The Lame One reined his horse about and hurried back to be with them. Once on land again, wiggling forward with the others, he drew closer and closer to that glittering curve of the waters, across which the Creeks' canoes lay tantalizingly empty and waiting.

He heard the two cannon, which the Pointed Arrow had brought, begin to thunder, spending their balls harmlessly enough, he had no doubt, against the breastwork of logs. The Americans would never win by frontal assault only. But there was another arrow for the General's bow. He, the Lame One, was part of that other arrow!

The Creeks were deceived by the masses of men before them, and Jackson's forces kept them so occupied they did not sense the danger on their rear. But into the river, one and another

Cherokee was slipping for the second time that day. After a little the canoes of the Creeks began to move away from their moorings, each guided by the hand of a strong swimmer. Then, loaded with Cherokees, and with friendly Creeks under Mc-Intosh, they came shooting back.

The Lame One heard the shout as the hostile Creeks discovered what was happening. From his place in a canoe, he could guess how they were rushing from the log ramparts now, back toward where the canoes had been waiting, ready to face their second foe, and hoping also to retrieve some of their only means of escape.

But it was too late. Their temporary panic gave opportunity — as the Lame One afterward learned — to Kaluna, the adopted son of John Jolly. Kaluna was over the ramparts, waving his sword and leaping among the Red Sticks as fearlessly as any Cherokee had ever leaped upon the enemy. Kaluna's platoon of whitemen were scrambling after him, but Kaluna went down with an arrow in his thigh.

"Rest," ordered the Pointed Arrow, when he saw Sam Houston on the ground covered with blood. One of his comrades had pulled out the arrow and the blood was spurting. Even as Andrew Jackson passed on, Kaluna, regardless of the order, was struggling to his feet.

The Creeks were brave fighters. Seeing the fortifications overrun they did the only possible thing. They separated into small groups. From the undergrowth they poured arrows, balls, spears and tomahawks upon the attackers. And every

Red Stick thought to himself of the assurance the medicine men had given them that very morning, assurance of perfect victory.

"Do not be concerned if for a time the battle shall seem to go against you. When a cloud shall come in the skies, then the tide will turn. So fight on. No matter how dark at times the outcome may appear, remember only this: the old magic and the strength of the old gods are at hand. These are all powerful."

There was need for strong magic. For the Cherokees and the Creeks under McIntosh were sweeping in upon the Red Sticks from the widest part of the horseshoe, the whites over its open neck.

The Lame One heard how Kaluna, up and fighting again, had led his men into a ravine where a covered redoubt housed some Creeks. A ball from one of their guns shattered the whiteman's right arm; another smashed the shoulder. The men about Kaluna disappeared in the undergrowth and would not rally, though the wounded one still urged them to follow him. Alone, the adopted son of the Cherokees climbed out of the ravine and collapsed.

The Creeks fought on stubbornly and searched the sky for the promised cloud, as they refused Pointed Arrow's offer of surrender. And finally a cloud appeared. There was even a flurry of rain. But the words of the medicine men did not come true. The tide of the battle did not turn.

A few severely wounded Creeks managed to slip into the river and swam down to the Great Swamp where the women were hidden. Then the sun set and suddenly there was a stillness. The last Creek on the island died as an Indian should. Not one begged for mercy.

A ridgepole fell in an empty, half-burned house. The Lame One who, in spite of his shortened leg, had been fighting all day, stopped and looked at the river. It was red with blood, red like a horseshoe heated in the fire. At that moment he sensed that the war with the Creeks was over. The Ridge had been right. About half of the Creek warriors must have been killed. The others no doubt would flee, perhaps to their friends, the Spaniards in Florida.

That night more details came to his ears. The Cherokees' own leader, Aganstata, was badly wounded. The Pointed Arrow was wounded slightly, while Kaluna was nigh to death. It would be a warrior's death and one of which any of the Cherokees would have been proud. Still, this fact did not keep the tears from John Jolly's eyes.

As to what had happened to Red Eagle, the leader of the Creeks, that was not known until two days later. Then the Lame One saw him come in proudly to Jackson's camp. Men leaped to their feet, guns in hand. Red Eagle looked scornful.

"I am a Creek and afraid of no man," he said as the guns went up. Not a hand pressed a trigger as Red Eagle went straight to the General's tent to plead for the starving Creek women and children.

Andrew Jackson treated his guest as a mighty warrior should

be treated. Red Eagle rode unharmed from that interview, while the Pointed Arrow declared, "Anyone who would kill a man as brave as that would rob the dead."

Years afterward the Cherokees were to remember that remark, and to wish that they themselves had killed the Pointed Arrow during the battle of Horseshoe Bend. Only they did not call him the Pointed Arrow then. With bitter hatred in their voices, they spoke of him as Chicken Snake. Snake was a word used for traitors.

As the warriors moved northward again, the Lame One thought over what had taken place. The Indians' way of fighting was the quick foray, the swift withdrawal. But the whites fought deliberately on and on, retreating only when absolutely necessary. Less glory but more certainty as to the end, this they had proved. No doubt the Americans would exact a large part of the Creeks' land as their reward when a peace was concluded. He wondered what, if anything, the Cherokees would receive. He did not think they need count on much!

He was glad the struggle was over. His leg pained him more than usual. Yet in other ways the days and the nights in the open, the association with men, the life of action had done much for him. He felt as though he could accomplish anything!

And then, on an hour when he was not even thinking of the task on which he had worked so long, he had the answer to the discovery that would help strengthen the Cherokee race — the key to the talking leaves. He was certain of the new revelation

— as certain as the Creeks had been that the old magic and the old gods would turn the tide of battle.

The Lame One threw back his head and laughed. The sound was so loud and prolonged that Agi-li rode over.

"I know how to do it!" cried the Lame One excitedly.

Agi-li still looked his question.

"To fashion wings for the Ground Squirrel! To play at last on the side of the Birds!"

The Chieftain of Willstown turned his horse about and rode away.

But the Lame One continued to laugh and to talk softly to himself. If the Cherokees would hold even a portion of their ancient heritage, they must learn the whiteman's art, they must learn to best the whiteman at the whiteman's game. Only the new ways would save them now. The failure of the Creek conjurers had proved the failure of the old spells.

All day long as he rode he thought about the answer to his problem. Every now and then his fingers moved as though tracing pictures in the air.

That was the day the Chieftain of Willstown made up his mind. When they returned to Willstown the Lame One must be married. He had persuaded his friend to one thing. Now he would persuade him to another. A wife would take this nonsense from him — that is, a wife who was demanding and clever. Agi-li's thoughts moved over the possibilities.

There was a woman named Sally. She was not young, but she had determination which would no doubt serve.

IX

The Naming of Sequoya

(Period ending February 1818)

THE LAME ONE was on his way to the Chickasaw council house. He was glad to go, to get away from his new wife. Sally was one who was forever saying, "You must do so and so! There must be this! There must be that!" It was her idea that a man should work for his wife, for his family, and not for the tribe. Besides, of what possible good to the tribe was this foolishness of his? She had never in all her life seen a man so possessed!

On a day before he went to the council Sally had been particularly bitter about the pieces of bark on which he was now carving marks with his knife. Some of the marks were copied from the whiteman's spelling book.

Before he left, therefore, the Lame One followed an inner impulse and did a strange thing. He took an old chest and fashioned a strong lock for it. Then he put the pieces of bark and the spelling book inside. The answer to the problem he had studied so long was coming now — slowly. He must not forget.

Perhaps, he thought wearily as he departed, it would be different after Sally's baby came. He hoped so.

The council brought new problems, and by the time he was on his way home once again, riding beside Archibald Campbell, he wished he had never gone from home. For he, with others of the Cherokees who had fought the Creeks, had been persuaded by Andrew Jackson, who met them at the council house, to sign a paper. The fifteen who had signed did so with marks like two crossed sticks, at the place where Andrew Jackson pointed.

As the Lame One was handed the quill he thought of the pictures he had drawn on the bark pieces. Then slowly, a trifle contemptuously, he made the sign of the crossed sticks as the others had done.

Whitemen talked very fast when they gave these papers to the Indians. But as far as the Lame One and his companions could figure out, what they had signed with the sticks promised the whitemen land lying to the west of their own far towns, land between the Tennessee, the Coosa and Turkey Creek. That meant less game, but the game had been disappearing fast, so perhaps it did not matter so much. Besides, the land had always been claimed by the Creeks, who declared the Cherokees had no right to it.

He noticed however that his comrades, who had imbibed freely of the liquor the whitemen had furnished them, were now by turn solemn or extremely voluble. "After all," one or another would say, "after all, nobody can blame us! What we have done is useless, because we insisted that the Cherokee Council at Turkeytown must agree to the signing away of this land, before it becomes lawful. That, we told the Pointed Arrow, was in accordance with Cherokee law. Only the chieftains in council can say in the end what shall be done. We could not speak for the tribe!"

The Lame One was thinking that the taking away of more land was poor reward for the help the Cherokees had given the Americans against the Creeks. While if the council at Turkeytown refused to agree to what he and his comrades had done, what then? Would he and the other signers be considered traitors like Doublehead? Hardly that, for the council had given them permission to go and adjust the disputed boundaries. Still he was both confused and troubled.

When he reached home, however, he forgot all about the paper. He forgot everything save the sight which met him. There in one corner the chest, which he had so carefully locked, stood with the cover thrown back. He knew before he looked that he would find it empty. No sign of the pieces of bark! No sign of the whiteman's book with the pictures on the first page, pictures which were important to him.

Sally watched him with no expression on her face. Only for a moment he saw her glance quickly toward the fireplace, while the fingers of one hand twisted the edge of her shawl a little tighter.

The Lame One looked toward the fire. There a heap of ashes told the story. Sally had seen to it that all he had done was gone forever. He understood as plainly as though she had spoken that she thought this destruction would stop his "foolishness," stop it conclusively.

But that could not be — not even though a dozen Sallys attempted it. He looked at the woman now as though she were a stranger.

"It must all be done over," he said.

He turned on his heel and went out of the cabin. To the deepest part of the woods he went and flung himself down. For hours he lay there, not thinking, stunned almost into insensibility. Yet in the end he must have slept. For suddenly he was awake and rested and thinking as usual of the marks he had been cutting on the bark.

Why, everything was all right. He could remember most of what he had done. And what he could not remember could be recreated. He must not waste time here any longer.

He returned, as fast as the lame leg permitted, to the cabin for his axe. He did not speak to Sally, but as he went forth with the axe on his shoulder, she sighed with relief.

She had done well when she followed the advice of the old men and destroyed everything in the chest. Now the spell-making was stopped. Her husband was angry with her still, but in time he would forget. Had he not gone to cut wood? She must remind him how close the winter was, and that they would need a sizable pile.

That day the Lame One did begin the felling of logs. But he used them not for wood for Sally's burning, but for timbers with which he built himself a cabin a little apart from Sally's. It was a small one-roomed affair, just large enough for his work and himself. There was a door which could be locked securely. There was a window which Sally could not reach. In one corner he would sleep. There was a rough table, a bench before it. And within reaching distance a shelf for his pipe.

A group of old men came to the edge of the clearing and watched as the Lame One worked. None offered to help. But when everything was done and the Lame One went inside and closed the door, there was an instant shower of stones on the roof.

The Lame One looked up astonished. For the stones were followed by a shower of words. After a moment he made some of them out.

"Ha-ya! Maker of spells, you of the Red Paint Clan! Sequoya! Sequoya!"

Into his puzzled bewilderment understanding came slowly. As plainly as though it were yesterday he could hear the medicine men in Tuskegee explaining: "Men who live alone are loathsome. They are like the polecat, the grinning opossum and the raincrow. They are fit only to associate with such creatures, and not with men of the seven clans."

So that was what the old men were saying. And "maker of spells!" They were afraid then of what he was doing. No wonder Agi-li had been confused and had tried to persuade him to leave his work. But now, there was time only for that work. It was no use to explain until it was finished. Besides the old ones would never believe him.

Sequoya! Of old the term had been used of the opossum. Then the Cherokees had applied the same word to the white-men's pigs. " 'Possum in a pen! Pig in a poke!" That was what they were saying of him. Well — that was what he was! What he must continue to be for a time. In the end they would understand.

Sequoya! He would bear that new name with honor, even though it had been given him in derision. Like all Cherokees the Lame One regarded a name as part of one's personality. Injury could result from the mishandling of a man's name. The old ones said he was making spells — well, in a sense he was. The spell he was making would, he hoped, turn aside the intentions of the old men when they called him Sequoya!

He pushed the table he had made underneath the window. On the floor was a pile of bark. He reached for a piece of the bark and for his knife. Then he gave himself up to his work. Time almost ceased to exist.

Now and then as the days, the weeks, the months passed, there were more showers of stones, more taunting words. But the man bending over his work scarcely heard. He was on the right trail — in a little while now, a little while . . . This pursuit of the talking leaves was like trailing an animal, a most elusive animal. After a bit he would have the creature securely trapped. He would follow his prey to the end. Sequoya! Sequoya!

He heard somehow, he could not remember just how, that the council at Turkeytown had agreed to the giving of land between the Tennessee, the Coosa and Turkey Creek. That was a relief. He could work better now.

He heard too that Sally's baby had arrived, and that it was a meal-sifter rather than a bow. But girl or boy, it did not matter. This that he was doing was more important. He never wondered how Sally managed to obtain food and fuel.

The neighbors however were helping and sharing with her, as they would with the poor, doing for her those tasks which would have been done for a woman whose husband was dead or ill. Neither gifts nor services were rendered cheerfully and this Sally knew. Under the circumstances she could not expect cheerfulness.

However, from a sense of duty — and because she saw that her husband's leg was swollen at the knee and seemed to bother him more than usual — she left a portion of the food beside the door of the small cabin. When he was hungry, so that his alertness lessened and he grew confused at his task, the Lame One — Sequoya — came out and ate.

The meal-sifter was big enough to toddle when he noticed her first. He held out a piece of bark and showed her the markings he had made with his knife. He pronounced the sound of each mark slowly. The baby seemed to comprehend. Her eyes sparkled. She grabbed his finger with one hand and held it tightly.

"Ah-yo-ka!" called Sally. That was how her father learned the meal-sifter's name. He set it down at once on a piece of bark. He smiled later when he read it.

After he had eaten, Sequoya reached for his green limestone pipe. From the weasel-skin pouch at his waist he took some dried red sumac leaves and thrust them into the bowl. Then, smoking slowly, he went over in his memory all the different carvings he had made, pictures not of individual words now, but of sounds.*

That was the revelation which had come to him on the way home from the war against the Red Sticks. Man's talk — Cherokee talk — was made up entirely of sounds, of different sounds. A single word might have one sound, or two, or four. But the same sound might go in a different word. There were many, many words. There were fewer sounds.

He uttered all the sounds he had mastered, slowly and softly, one by one, while his eyes remained closed, thinking as he said them of the picture he had cut in bark for each sound. He kept track of the number with his fingers. And when he had used all his fingers, he made a single mark on the ground beside him and started over. Finally he gave the last sound of all, the hiss of a snake. That hissing sound was used so many times he could save many pictures by fitting the hiss into place on sound-pictures he already knew. He knew from the marks on the ground that

* Syllables

he had counted the fingers of both hands eight times — eight times and six fingers over. He had remembered them all!

It was growing dark when he stood up, stretching his arms high above his head. He was tired. He had not realized until now how tired. Tomorrow when his mind was clear, he would check his memory once more. Then he would know if he had finally found the answer — whether at last he had trapped the secret he had trailed so long.

Suddenly he longed for the woods, for the inner peace which he had never failed to find there. Ah-yo-ka came running toward him again. He bent and patted her cheek.

"Tomorrow," he said.

Sally called the child sharply.

Sequoya loosened the fingers which still clung, turned and walked swiftly toward the shadows. The door of his little cabin swung open behind him. He had ended his quest. He had achieved the impossible. He, Sequoya, had done it. Yet he felt no joy. Rather there was a strange foreboding, a sense of dark clouds about him. Even the wood was not as he had expected. Its peace was troubled.

Surely, he assured himself. It will be easy now to explain what I have been doing.

But to teach others what he had learned? There was a sudden doubt. He had been so long alone. He had used words one by one. The art of the storyteller, the ability to persuade others, he felt, was gone. Perhaps it was gone forever.

Besides, the old men hated him. He would guess how they were spreading their evil tales. He had a dread now of going forth among his fellows. He understood how they must feel toward him, a crippled one. If there were only a place far off, where he could be away from malicious tongues for a time — could regain his strength and confidence, could teach those who did not disbelieve at the very beginning. Disbelief and maliciousness fashioned a strong spell. No one had to know any formulas to understand that.

He slept, yet the sleep was not peaceful. He dreamed of the time he had first fled from Tuskegee with Wurteh and had looked back over her shoulder, watching long snakes of smoke spiraling upward.

He woke, sniffing that smoke and it was real. Furtively he slipped back toward his cabin. Then suddenly he threw himself on the ground and crept forward until he was hidden behind a screen of thick laurel. He understood now why he had dreamed of smoke!

In the clearing before him where his cabin had stood was a crowd of old men, laughing and shrilling at one another and poking a great heap of ashes. The heap of ashes was all that remained of the cabin where he had spent the last two summers and winters.

Sequoya! Sequoya! The 'possum was unhoused! The pig had lost his poke! The old men had done what they had wanted to do for so long. They had destroyed the place where the son of Wurteh of the Red Paint Clan was making his dark magic.

The hidden one wormed himself closer so he could hear what they were saying.

"It is Sequoya who has set the Nation at odds. Because of his spell-making John Jolly and his friends have come begging us to give up the country where we have always dwelt, give up the mountain land of our fathers for worthless land in the west."

"Ha-yu! I myself heard that the White Father will give a gun, a blanket and a kettle to all who will leave their cabins here and go over the Great River, so anxious the whitemen are to be rid of us. There they say we can take up hunting and live as our fathers lived and be happy again."

"It is all a lie. There is no good hunting there. Besides, there are many of us who are farmers and raise cattle and pigs. We do not want to take up hunting again. The farmers are furious at the idea."

"I know, I know. It is all a spell, the spell of Sequoya to destroy the Cherokee Nation."

"The Ridge himself says we should never give up our land here. And John Ross echoes his words."

"Ha-yu! Still there are many who are going with Jolly. The Nation will be divided. We shall grow weak and helpless like the Creeks, we, the Principal People. You will see. Worse things will follow. We have burned the pen, but it is too late. The evil has gone forth."

The listener in the bushes was sick at heart. He must go to Agi-li and tell him what he had accomplished during this time he had stayed by himself. He understood at last how far the bitterness of the old men had taken them. They would never listen to him now, but they might listen to Agi-li.

He slipped back into the woods and ran all the way to the house of his friend.

However the moment he entered he knew that Agi-li was not pleased to see him. He was sitting with his head in his hands, and at sight of the visitor he frowned. There were important matters to think about. He could not be bothered with trifles, he interrupted, when the visitor started to explain.

"Go away for a time. Get out doors and drive the cobwebs from your brain."

Agi-li might have paid more attention, but he too was worried. Long ago President Jefferson had suggested that the Indians should leave the eastern land. Then it had been only talk. But now it seemed as though practically all the whitemen about the Cherokees, and those in Washington as well, had determined that the Cherokees should go over the Mississippi. And Big John Jolly — with his smile, his beaming face and his glowing descriptions of the land beyond the Mississippi, his pleas that only by the giving up of some of the eastern land would the Government at Washington agree to protect the Cherokees already there from the enemy tribes — Big John Jolly had spoken too eloquently. He had persuaded the Chieftain of Willstown, as well as Charley Hicks and others in the east, to sign a treaty which agreed to exchanging part of the Cherokee land in the east for other land beyond the Great River. A part of the yearly annuity due the Cherokees for the many pieces of land they had already given up was also to go to the Western Cherokees.

Andrew Jackson had been at the treaty-signing, arguing plausibly: "Those who move west go to a country belonging to the United States." He meant by that of course that no separate state had claim to it. "There your lands can never be taken from you. To that we will agree. But here in the east you have only hunting rights." Long years ago, Jackson claimed, the Cherokees had arranged for an exchange of eastern lands for land in the west.

The Cherokees remembered no such agreement. They remembered only that a few years before the Government had paid the way of some of their number to go to the west, to see how fine the lands were in that distant country.

But Andrew Jackson shook his head and smiled, that strange smile of his which could mean anything. The Government, he declared, was very kind in offering to move the Indians now, free of charge, to say nothing of furnishing them with guns and ammunition. For those who were poor and wanted them, there would probably be plows and things like that. As for their cabins or such things which they left behind in the east, when these were of any value, the White Father would pay for them. And of course those who wanted to might stay in the east and become Americans.

Oh, the treaty had been done properly and in council, and there John Ross, who was a young man, had spoken out against it. He declared the greater number of the Cherokees were no longer interested in living as their fathers had done. They had taken up the whiteman's way and intended to continue. Most of them wanted to remain where the woods, the mountains, the streams were familiar. There the Indian was part of the country itself.

Ross had no standing in the council, but The Ridge, that great orator, was shoulder to shoulder with him against the exchange, and The Ridge could sway men with his speaking. A paper was sent out protesting the treaty and it was signed by chieftains and men of importance from sixty-seven towns. The Government at Washington paid no attention to this paper and said only that the treaty was already in effect. That part of the land in the east which the treaty covered was gone. But the new land across the Mississippi was ready and waiting.

There was great bitterness in the Nation. The people in the northern part, who were better farmers than those in the far towns, wanted to separate entirely from the far towns, to divide the Eastern Nation in two. It was, they declared angrily, the chieftains in the south who had done this thing.

Agi-li, remembering why, in the old days, he had come to Willstown, could see both sides. He reproached himself for signing the treaty. And he knew that Charley Hicks did likewise. If only the Cherokees could understand the tricks in the whitemen's treaties, then they would not get themselves and the Nation into trouble.

Dark days, he felt, were ahead. He could not be bothered now with small matters. So he shook his head and turned away from his old friend.

"I am busy," he said.

With bent shoulders the Lame One left the Chieftain of Willstown. He felt old and useless. Perhaps he had been wrong to spend so much time on one thing. Perhaps the time had been wasted. Perhaps.

Stubbornly he shook his head. He knew what he had accomplished. Agi-li had failed him. But there must be another way.

That night he sought out John Jolly.

And when in February, Jolly's flotilla of nineteen flatboats moved down the Tennessee, Sequoya was among those Cherokees leaving for the Western Land. He was fleeing — he thought wryly, remembering the old men — from the hunters once more. Only this time the hunters were his own people.

Then out of the past came other wisdom to comfort him.

In the old days, so it was said, the bears were a part of the Cherokee tribe. But the bears grew more and more different from the rest of the tribe. So they decided at last to leave their relatives and go and live in the forest. Before parting they turned to the Cherokees and said, "It is better for you that we should go; but we will teach you songs, and some day when you are in need, come out to the woods and sing these songs. Then we shall appear and help you."

The time was coming, Sequoya felt certain, when the Nation would need terribly that which he could give them. So he must teach his "song" to those in the west. Then he would return east with his gift.

X

Ah-yo-ka

(1821)

THE TSI'-KILILI' was singing. But Agi-li did not hear. He was lost in his own brooding. His mood was dark and dismal. The Chieftain of Willstown had a right to be discouraged. During the past three years the whiteman's smothering blanket was closing in about the Creeks in Georgia. After the Creeks were driven out, Agi-li felt certain would come the turn of the Cherokees. The greater part of these now lived within the boundaries of that state.

It was sad about the Creeks. In spite of the fact that the friendly Creeks under McIntosh had fought with the Americans against their own countrymen, they had paid a heavy price for the warring of their brothers. It had just come to Agi-li's ears that the whites had secured a great stretch of "Georgia territory" from them. Only a tract around Indian Spring where the treaty had been made, and about the home of the Chieftain

McIntosh, had been spared. It was queer about that tract around the McIntosh home.

The Creeks were suspicious of their leader and bitter about what had happened. They declared they would not yield another inch of land to the whites. In council they passed a law similar to the old custom of the Cherokees. It condemned to death any Creek who sold tribal lands without the approval of the council. What was not done in the public square, the Creeks declared, would not be binding upon their people.

On the other hand, the whitemen were saying loudly that the Creeks' land in Georgia must all belong to them. No other state had such an Indian burden. Thousands of Creeks and Cherokees! It was not fair. Was there to be no opportunity for Georgia's young men? No lands for their taking?

Besides, at the turn of the century the Government of the United States had demanded certain western land from Georgia which the Government had received.* In return Washington had agreed to extinguish the Indians' title to land in Georgia's reduced boundaries, and give that land to Georgia as soon as this could be done "peaceably and on reasonable terms." It was time, Georgia decided, that the promise be kept. The Indians must go. They did not cultivate the land anyhow, not to any extent. Let them be sent elsewhere. There had been plenty of Indian tribes moved westward — beyond the Mississippi. Let the Creeks be moved too. The Creeks were barbarians. All the Indians were barbarians!

* This territory later became the states of Alabama and Mississippi. Georgia's title however was not clear. Spain claimed the lands at the time of Georgia's "session."

True enough, Agi-li reminded himself, the Cherokee lands were in the mountains and not nearly as desirable as those the Creeks held. But let the Creeks yield — and he had a feeling it was inevitable that they would yield or be maneuvered out of their final holdings — once that happened, what about the Cherokees?

He was thankful they had such leaders as The Ridge and Ross. The Ridge was typical of the best of the old full-bloods, he was the son of Oconostota, a great warrior. While Ross, with a white father and two white grandfathers, was trained in the whiteman's ways and clever at playing the whiteman's game.

At this point in his thinking, Agi-li became conscious of the tsi'kilili's song and of a knocking at the door. Both song and knocking had been continuing for some time. But before he could rise to answer, the door opened and a stranger stood there.

He was tall and slender of build. His face was thin, his eyes eager. He was dressed in a warm mantle, which swung open and Agi-li saw the buckskin tunic, the long leggings to his hips. Unornamented moccasins were on his feet. About his head was a cloth turban bound neatly. Such garb was not common any longer among the Eastern Cherokees.

Not until the man stepped forward, hand outstretched, did Agi-li recognize him from the limp in his walk. It was the Lame One — Sequoya, the old men at Willstown had called him contemptuously. And unthinking, "Sequoya!" was the name which fell from Agi-li's lips.

The newcomer did not seem to mind. Instead he smiled easily.

"A-ya! Sequoya! I am just back from the Western Land where I went to bring you proof of what I was doing in my cabin here when the old men gave me that name. See, here is the proof. It is a letter from your son beyond the Mississippi. It is sealed and I have never seen it. This I say for truth. Yet if you will break the seal and open it now, I will read you every word which is set down — *in Cherokee!*"

The last words were said slowly and very quietly. At the same time they came forth as triumphant as a successful warrior's cry.

"I have asked your son," continued Sequoya, "to write especially of matters of which I have no knowledge; of family concerns kept inside your house door. I have begged him to remind you of days and adventures which only you two have shared. I do not know one thing he has written. But whatever is there I will read to you.

"I have brought other letters. . ." He gestured toward the skin-wrapped pack he had left on the doorstone. "These too are written to friends and relatives in Willstown from those who have gone beyond the Mississippi. But I came to you first."

Agi-li did not attempt to conceal his dismay. The man had returned then still deluded. He recalled now hearing that he was back at Sally's cabin. And it was true that the woman had not come to him recently asking aid of any sort. Even Sally, it must be, had been glad to welcome her husband. While as for the child, Ah-yo-ka, someone had said she had been pleased beyond the telling, and that father and child were inseparable.

Agi-li did not know quite how to handle the situation. He must learn more before he decided. So the Chieftain of Willstown shook his head.

"I am busy — perhaps later I can come to you."

"When?" demanded Sequoya, the Lame One, remembering that before he had departed for the west with John Jolly, the Chieftain of Willstown had said, "I am busy."

"Soon. In a week or so."

"I shall wait for your coming," said the visitor and departed.

Agi-li had been unprepared for the quiet acceptance. He had, when he spoke, no idea of going to Sally's cabin. Yet he had given his promise, and promises were something to be kept. Besides, the news which he continued to hear was puzzling to say the least.

The returned one was industrious. He was working at the crops, providing for Sally and the child. The pile of wood he was cutting was a sight to see. Only occasionally was he observed carving marks on pieces of bark, but that seemed to be something he was doing for Ah-yo-ka's pleasure. The child hung over his shoulder when he did it, chattering and pointing. Perhaps he was making pictures for her. He had been good at making pictures in the old days. Even now one could recognize his silverwork because of the designs.

After all, decided Agi-li, he had been abrupt. There would

be no harm in stopping by, in praising the returned one's industry.

Sequoya was glad to see him. He went at once for the letter. It was sealed, as whitemen's letters are sealed. And there were many pages.

Agi-li took them and handled them curiously. They were not in whitemen's writing, so much was clear, for he had seen that often enough at the councils. He had watched Charley Hicks setting matters down again and again in the whiteman's fashion. He had watched his nephew, David Brown, trying to put down Cherokee words in whiteman's letters, words which Agi-li pronounced over and over for him.

David, Agi-li recalled, had grown very discouraged. Some words he could not put down at all, and when he pronounced what he had, the words did not sound in the least like Cherokee to Agi-li, although often he did not say so.

Now Agi-li stared again at the paper before him. Suddenly he lifted it to his nose and sniffed. It smelled like his son — there was a certain way he mixed sumac with wild tobacco!

Sequoya smiled. Then, taking the papers from Agi-li, the Lame One began to read, slowly but confidently. Sentence after sentence in perfect Cherokee fell from his lips. His voice was certain and sure, and musical as the tsi′-kilili′s singing.

Agi-li was astonished. For many things which Sequoya was saying Agi-li had never told to anyone. Only his son could know them.

However, as the voice of the Lame One continued, Agi-li's expression changed. Ha-yu! He was beginning to understand! He listened more carefully than before, watching the Lame One and nodding his head as though in agreement.

When Sequoya finished the last of the closely covered sheets, he folded them and looked at Agi-li with calm expectancy.

"This is most interesting, Sequoya. But I see nothing new in it."

"You — see — nothing — new?"

"No."

For a time the other did not speak. Astonishment and dismay mingled on his face. But surely Agi-li had not understood. This was a letter from his son, written in the Cherokee language. He, the Lame One, had taught him, as he had taught others in the west.

He opened his lips to try once again to explain. But Agi-li waved him to silence. "You were ever a good one at remembering and you have learned this thing. These are not words set down which you read, but blazes such as whitemen make on trees to guide you. They are like the beads on wampum belts, which are not words, but guides to make one remember.

"Cannot I myself read the wampum belts of Old Echota? And does it not take a long time and many words for me to read the belts which the Iroquois brought from the north in the old days when we were young? This I learned in my youth when the chieftains sent our young men to the wise ones. The different beads and the way they were placed in the belt meant certain things. While in the attached strings, the placing of the beads meant something else altogether. The length of those strings, the width of the belts — all these were important.

"No, I see nothing new, nothing strange in what you have done. It is your memory you are trusting and the marks are guides you have. Just as the poles or heaps of stones which we set up at different places recall to the passer-by all the things that happen there. You may not intend to deceive, but you do when you say that you have never seen these papers before. You must have. You are only remembering."

"That is not true! I can read! And I do say again that I have never seen these pages before!"

"Think once more. You must have seen them, though you may have forgotten. For a long time many of us have understood that you were ill, though the old men have thought otherwise. Now it is proved that we who thought you were ill were right. Only an ill man could make himself believe such tales."

"I am not ill," protested Sequoya. "Look. This is the sound for Tsa- Ꮳ And this for gi- Ꭹ." He drew the syllables quickly on a piece of paper, using a quill pen standing in a small gourd of ink on the table. He had long used the quill and the ink. It was easier thus, and in the west, the chieftains had been proud to supply him when they learned what he was doing.

"This is the way I put them together and say this word — Tsa-gi!" **ᏣᎩ**

"Here, Agi-li, is your name."

ᎠᎩᏟ

The writer's fingers moved fast, as though by their very swiftness he must convince the one before him.

"Besides, I do forget what I have written. I put it down and lay it aside. I forget all about it. When, perhaps, a long time has passed, I take up the paper again. And I can read there things I have forgotten."

Agi-li was not convinced. He watched the Lame One almost pityingly. Ah-yo-ka came into the room and slipped to her father's side. Neither of the men paid any attention to her. Ah-yo-ka had now known six summers.

The child stood watching what her father was doing. He cast one paper on which he had been writing aside and it fell to the floor. Ah-yo-ka picked it up and began talking to herself as her eyes went over the letters. Suddenly her small voice broke through her father's — as the sound of a brook can often be heard trickling above the roar of a nearby river.

"Wait," said Agi-li. "What is the child saying?"

"What is she saying? She is reading what I have written, as I have written it."

"But she cannot. She is young and she has not seen this before. Unless you always make the same pictures."

"I do not. Wait. I will show her the letter I brought you. She has never seen that. But perhaps she can read — some of it at least, though your son's writing is different from mine, not so clearly drawn I think."

He handed the letter to Ah-yo-ka. And after a little pucker of her lips and her forehead, she began to read the very words which Sequoya had uttered. As she grew accustomed to the new writing her voice went more smoothly.

"Yo!" Agi-li jumped to his feet and began to pace the room. In quick succession his face mirrored disbelief and astonishment, fear and delight, hope and dismay.

If — if it were true! Then the Cherokees who had traveled so far away would not have gone entirely out of the lives of their kinsmen and friends. Then — those in the eastern mountains, near the old town of Keetoowah, who could not come often to the council fires, would have a way of sending news back and forth, of keeping old ties. Aye, that was it. If the Cherokees could keep the old ties, could remain united as one people, then the Nation would never be broken in pieces as the red bundles of sticks from the prophet, Tecumseh, had been broken.

Agi-li turned and held out his hand to Sequoya.

"I shall reserve my decision," he said. He looked straight at Sequoya and was silent for several minutes.

The Lame One waited. There was a new look in Agi-li's eyes. It might betoken much. At length the Chieftain of Willstown spoke a second time.

"I shall try to persuade the chieftains. Nay, I promise more. I will persuade them to one thing. We will send the young men to you!"

As soon as these words were spoken, Sequoya realized that at last he had come nearly to the end of his quest. For when Agi-li gave a promise one could depend upon it. At last he had fashioned wings for the Flying Squirrel, but more important he had brought his people a song to sing when they needed it. Aid for the Cherokee Nation! This was all that mattered!

As the young men had come in the old days to the wise, the instructed ones, at Echota, that Blessed Peace Town, to learn the reading of wampum, so now they would come to him, to learn his talking leaves.

Sequoya looked down at his daughter and smiled. He had taught Ah-yo-ka. He could teach the young men.

That night as Agi-li lay sleepless, words came back to him from the wampum belts of deerskin which the Iroquois had brought to Echota, words he had read again and again at the council from the shell beads strung on sinew. The Iroquois from the north who had come seeking peace had said then that a big light must be kindled so they might recognize each other at a long distance — a light to be seen in the dark.

Was this a light then, which was to be seen by the Cherokees — a light when they greatly needed it, to guide them in whatever should happen, even if they should lose their Eastern Land? A light which should lead them to a council where they would be one people?

In the old days too the messengers of peace had said: "We will make a path for you to travel in, and the rising generation may do the same — we also will keep it swept clean and white, so that the rising generation may travel in peace."

Agi-li drew in his breath sharply. What kind of path might the rising generation of the Cherokees have to travel? Would it be clean and white, and would they travel in peace? Or would that path be, as he feared, rough and full of pitfalls?

Agi-li drew his hand across his forehead. He had thought enough about the wampum belts. That was knowledge he had learned long ago, and now after all the intervening years he could remember, even without the wampum belts to guide him.

Before he fell asleep he thought about his promise to the Lame One and was glad he had given it. If there was new knowledge, the young men could learn it. If it were but illusion and imagination, the young men were keen. All he could do was to wait and help test the young men when they came from Sequoya.

Would they come forth excited and pleased with what they had learned? Or would they come forth laughing and shrugging their shoulders, repeating derisively, as he had heard it so often repeated, the word Sequoya?

XI

The Chieftains Send Their Young Men

(1821)

THE YOUNG MEN were coming. Tall and slender they were, most of them, walking firmly and easily on strong legs, and with a pride in their Indian heritage which the white-men — and in some cases, even white blood — had not eradicated.

Their eyes were sharp and missed nothing, though they kept their faces immobile, and pretended not to be curious. Perhaps only one trained to observe since childhood, as Sequoya had been trained, would have caught those tiny flashes of derision, the lips' almost imperceptible quirks of disdain and annoyance.

Such signs were more apt to come from those Indians who had been at the missionary schools, the one at Springplace, the newer one at Brainerd. Word had reached these students that Sequoya had declared the method he had discovered was easy to learn; that Cherokees in the west had learned both to read and write in a few days.

Such a statement was absurd. *They* had learned to read and write, to say nothing of spelling, and understood well enough how difficult a task it was. It required at least several years. This unlettered one could not possibly have done what he claimed. It might be foolish for the old men to call it witchcraft. Still, they could scarcely be blamed.

Yet word had gone through the Nation and they had been ordered to come and pay attention to what the Lame One had to tell them. The Chieftain of Willstown desired it, and George Lowry was increasingly powerful at the councils.

So here they were! If the man attempted to trick them, they would not hesitate to speak out against him. If he were, as the old ones declared, a sorcerer making evil spells, there were those among them who felt strong enough to hold out against such spells, no matter how powerful. These would give testimony and the chieftains would order the man put to death. They all knew that such a death would be a horrible one. Even a Cherokee might well be afraid to die thus.

Yet the man waiting quietly before them showed no signs of fear. He was watching them closely, yes, and once or twice there seemed to be the ghost of a twinkle in his eyes.

Ah-yo-ka, his small daughter, was beside him. And when Sequoya bent and said something in her ear, Ah-yo-ka nodded and laughed aloud.

"Now," said Sequoya, when the young men were all seated at

some long tables which had been made ready, "I have worked for a long time and I have discovered how to put down Cherokee talk in much the same fashion as whitemen put down their talk. The whitemen have long used their knowledge to advantage; it will be a good thing for Cherokees to have such knowledge to use also.

"I have taught Cherokees in the west. And they have sent messages to their friends and kinsmen here in the east. I would like to teach you to read what they have written.

"Ah-yo-ka has learned already. She can read what is set down, no matter what it may be. I shall send her away now, but I will write whatever you tell me to write and she will come back and read it aloud to you."

There was no dearth of messages. Sequoya put them down, one at a time, and Ah-yo-ka would come and, standing beside her father, read what was there. Even when the young men kept her apart from Sequoya and carried the papers to her, she read them just as easily.

Next Sequoya held up before them some boards, planed smooth and fastened together to make a surface as wide as a deerskin. On this he had painted many small pictures. Each was simple in outline, and each, he explained, stood for a different sound.*

As their eyes ran over the pictures, some of the young men who had been to the missionary schools laughed aloud. "You have whiteman's letters there, and some of them are upside down and

* Syllable

backside-to. As for J — you have used that letter several times."

"Yo! You are to forget while you are here what you have learned in the whiteman's school. *This is Cherokee talk.* These are not letters as you call them, though it is true I have taken some of them from the whiteman's book. I have used them in different fashions, yes. Others I have made up out of

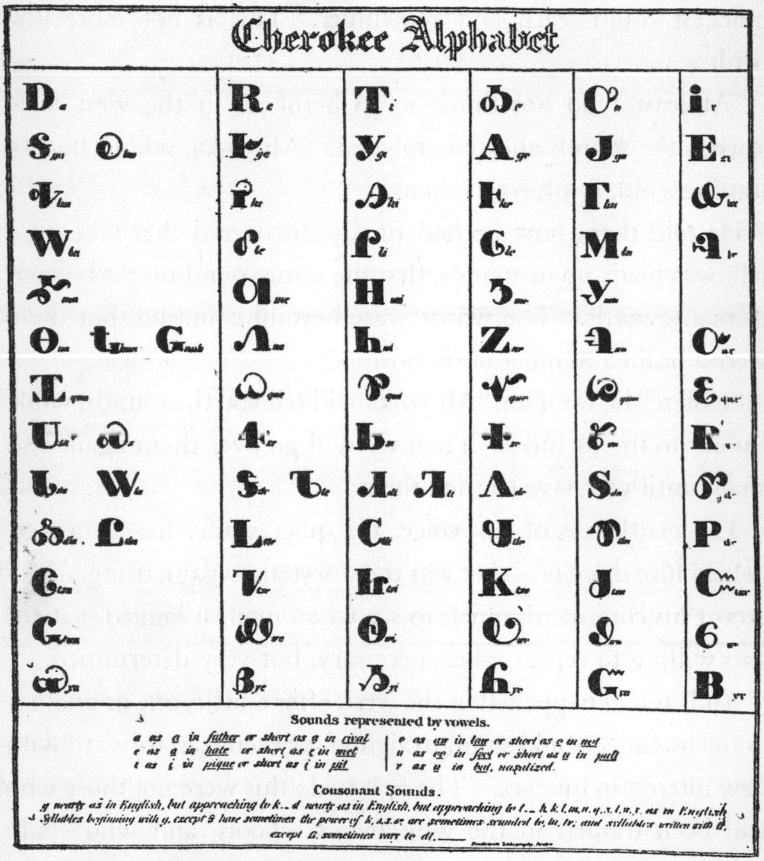

Cherokee Alphabet

Ꭰ a	Ꭱ e	Ꭲ i	Ꭳ o	Ꭴ u	Ꭵ v
Ꭶ ga Ꭷ ka	Ꭸ ge	Ꭹ gi	Ꭺ go	Ꭻ gu	Ꭼ gv
Ꭽ ha	Ꭾ he	Ꭿ hi	Ꮀ ho	Ꮁ hu	Ꮂ hv
Ꮃ la	Ꮄ le	Ꮅ li	Ꮆ lo	Ꮇ lu	Ꮈ lv
Ꮉ ma	Ꮊ me	Ꮋ mi	Ꮌ mo	Ꮍ mu	
Ꮎ na Ꮏ hna Ꮐ nah	Ꮑ ne	Ꮒ ni	Ꮓ no	Ꮔ nu	Ꮕ nv
Ꮖ qua	Ꮗ que	Ꮘ qui	Ꮙ quo	Ꮚ quu	Ꮛ quv
Ꮜ s Ꮝ sa	Ꮞ se	Ꮟ si	Ꮠ so	Ꮡ su	Ꮢ sv
Ꮣ da Ꮤ ta	Ꮥ de Ꮦ te	Ꮧ di Ꮨ ti	Ꮩ do	Ꮪ du	Ꮫ dv
Ꮬ dla Ꮭ tla	Ꮮ tle	Ꮯ tli	Ꮰ tlo	Ꮱ tlu	Ꮲ tlv
Ꮳ tsa	Ꮴ tse	Ꮵ tsi	Ꮶ tso	Ꮷ tsu	Ꮸ tsv
Ꮹ wa	Ꮺ we	Ꮻ wi	Ꮼ wo	Ꮽ wu	Ꮾ wv
Ꮿ ya	Ᏸ ye	Ᏹ yi	Ᏺ yo	Ᏻ yu	Ᏼ yv

Sounds represented by vowels.

a as *a* in *father* or short as *a* in *rival* | *o* as *aw* in *law* or short as *o* in *not*
e as *a* in *hate* or short as *e* in *met* | *u* as *oo* in *fool* or short as *u* in *pull*
i as *i* in *pique* or short as *i* in *pit* | *v* as *u* in *but*, nasalized.

Consonant Sounds.

g nearly as in English, but approaching to k.. d nearly as in English, but approaching to t.. h, k, l, m, n, q, s, t, w, y, as in English. Syllables beginning with g, except Ꭶ have sometimes the power of k; Ꭰ, Ꮝ, Ꮧ are sometimes sounded to, tu, tv; and syllables written with tl, except Ꮭ, sometimes vary to dl.

my head. But to me these are pictures of sounds. While you are here they must be the same to you.

"To learn this talk so it can be remembered is like tracking an animal which is clever and full of tricks. It is like following a new trail where nothing is known.

"Now in the days when I was young, the young men came to those who already knew, to learn to read wampum belts. The quickest could learn and remember. This is not more difficult.

"At least I do not think so. Cherokees in the west have learned the sounds and remembered. Ah-yo-ka, who is but six summers old, has learned them."

He told them how he had finally discovered that Cherokee talk was made up of sounds, that the same sound might be used in many words. The words were beyond counting, but there were a limited number of sounds.

"Listen," he went on, "Ah-yo-ka will tell you the sounds, while I point to the pictures. Then we will go over them again and again until you have learned them."

The gentleness of his voice, his quiet smile, his assurance, helped lure them on. He was the storyteller again, using all the arts at his command, quick to see when interest lagged, patient and willing to repeat when necessary, but very determined.

And, as had happened in the west, after a little, one or another of the listeners would sit up straighter, or even lean forward with new interest in his eyes. The first to do this were not those who had been trained in the whiteman's schools, and who could already read and write. It was more difficult for these because some of the letters were already impressed on their minds in the whiteman's fashion. Those who had no training had nothing to forget.

There was paper on the tables before them. There were gourds filled with ink, and piles of quill pens. There were pieces of bark.

Sequoya had gone over the signs patiently. Now, as though tired, he paused for a few minutes. Knives were coming out. The paper was disregarded, so were the pieces of bark. The full-bloods began cutting into the wood of the tables.

"I can do it!" cried one. "Look! I have written my name — here in the wood."

He was tremendously excited. It was something to write one's name!

"And I!"

"And I!"

Those who had been trained in the missionary schools would not be outdone. They seized the quills, dipped them into the ink, and drew their names in the Cherokee symbols on paper, one symbol for each syllable.

It was easy. And the name was much shorter in Cherokee than in the whiteman's letters. Perhaps the man did have something after all. The missionaries' students showed their astonishment plainly.

Sequoya had waited a long time for this day. The "Bear" had come back and was teaching his song. The witch was working his spell. Patiently he went over and over the pictures. And then, when the young men thought they had learned them, so they could say them in chorus with no hesitation, his finger would dart from one to another.

Then instead of saying them the young men must write down the sounds as he called them aloud. This was slower work. Some could not manage the ink easily, so they used their knives and the bark as Sequoya showed them. A knife feels comfortable in a man's fingers. And the pictures were easy to cut. Sequoya had made them so.

Then the pictures before them were taken away. The young men must remember without them. But if one forgot, his neighbor might have that very sound in his name, so of course *he* remembered. The one who forgot copied from his neighbor until that which had been forgotten was fast in his own head.

Day in and day out for seven days the instructing went on. Each day there was more excitement. Race after race was run there on the table, races between minds and fingers. Before the young men were ready to face the council, every one of them had won some of those races. Those whose fingers were slow had the best memories. And those who had been trained in the whiteman's school, made the best pictures — for a time. Then the others caught up. The young men had come and the young men had learned!

At the end of the seventh day when Sequoya held forth his hands palm upward to show that he had no more to give them, a shout went up.

"Sequoya! Sequoya! Sequoya!"

'Possum in a pen! Pig in a poke! It was a name to bear proudly!

The young men were cheering for themselves as well. They too had trapped the wild creature which their master had trailed so long. The Cherokee language — the talking leaves belonged to them.

Even those who had been to the missionary schools said: "This talk is better than what the whiteman has. It is easier to learn and once we have learned the sounds, we can both write and read them. There is nothing here such as the whitemen call spelling. There are no letters which are not needed. There are no tricks. What Sequoya has found is simple. It is clear as water in a spring."

But those who had not gone to the whitemen's schools looked at Sequoya. Some of them laughed and said, "We can write and we can read! We can write letters to each other! And we can read letters too!"

And one who until then had not uttered a word burst out in a voice carrying above all the others: "It is a very great wonder!"

"A very great wonder!" Sequoya had heard those words that night on the Wabash. They made him remember that journey. In his memory it had seemed always to have been in two parts, the trail from Echota to the Ohio was one part; and from the Ohio to the Wabash another.

This day he had completed half of another journey. He had

taught the young men. Now he and the young men must go to the council at Oostanaula.

There the chieftains were waiting for the report of those who had been with Sequoya. There the old men were gathering to see what sort of a spell had been put upon those sent to the witch. They were waiting too for the death sentence upon the spell-maker.

He must persuade the chieftains. And they must satisfy the old men. That was the second part of his journey — his journey for which it had taken him ten years to make ready.

At Oostanaula the chieftains sat in a circle beneath a great arbor covered with tree branches. Charley Hicks was beside Pathkiller as usual. There were those among the chieftains who were waiting anxiously for the young men. These were the fathers whom the old men had made fearful of Sequoya's power. Agi-li was watching the fathers closely.

But when the young men came, it was clear to everyone that they were unharmed. There was respect in the manner in which they surrounded Sequoya, which, the Chieftain of Willstown saw, was like to that which the chieftains had for Pathkiller and for Charley Hicks.

Then, unbidden, the thought came to Agi-li of Old Tassel, that Beloved One. And thinking of Old Tassel he remembered the ancient story of the birds and the animals in the ball game. He nearly laughed aloud, for all at once he understood what Sequoya had meant when he talked of making wings for the Ground Squirrel.

And to think that he himself had so nearly been persuaded by the old men that Sequoya was mad! Mad? Why the Lame One was greater than them all! He had dared death itself to bring the talking leaves to his people. Agi-li drew in his breath sharply. The young men must make the chieftains understand. He turned and looked at them once more. Then he breathed easily. There was no need for concern.

For the young men held their heads high with pride like warriors in the old days who bore scalps at their belts; like hunters who had made a good kill. The young men were like fresh horses, eager and ready to take the trail.

Pathkiller himself questioned them.

"We speak the truth," was their reply. "Sequoya can put Cherokee talk on paper and he has taught us how to do it. There is no witchcraft about the matter."

One after another declared the same thing in different words.

The old men crowded close to the rail in back of the chieftains. Their eyes were little and mean. Their lips were pinched and their voices shrill.

"He has bewitched you too, all of you!"

"He has not bewitched us," reminded Pathkiller. And the chieftains nodded. "Let us see and hear what this is all about."

The Pathkiller ordered the young men placed at one side of the council, and Sequoya at the other.

"Can you write to Sequoya, write in Cherokee, the things which we will tell you?" he asked the young men.

"We can."

The chieftains one after another told the young men what to say. And whatever it was, no matter how secret, and no matter which young man set it down, Sequoya read it aloud when it was brought to him.

Then the chieftains told Sequoya to write to the young men. And they told him too what they wanted him to write.

The young men could read whatever was brought them.

Next the young men were separated and wrote to each other. That too was successful. Finally the chieftains could think of no more tests, so they asked the old men whether they were satisfied.

The old men mumbled among themselves. After several minutes one of them spoke. "I have a story which was told to my grandfather when he was young. He said he had told it to no one but me. And I have told it to no one. Write this story to Sequoya. If he can read that, then I will believe!"

A young man put it down and Sequoya read it easily. Then other young men to whom it was shown read it too. The old man's mouth fell open and it stayed open for a long time.

"Show us how it is done," said the chieftains.

Sequoya said, "I could show you, but the young men can show you as well as I. Let the young men do it."

So those who had been learners became teachers. They showed the chieftains, and the chieftains began writing their names. So did the old men — some of them. A few who had talked the most about Sequoya would not even try. They had not come to the council to learn anything. They had come to see a witch put to death.

The council at Oostanaula was a council no longer. It had become a school. There was great excitement. Some of the most reserved chieftains lay back on the ground and laughed. The whites had befuddled them all these years with the setting of their strange marks on paper. Now the Cherokees could put down their own marks. Not a whiteman would know what they meant.

Suddenly one among them burst forth with a shout. "I can write to my son who went away so long ago."

A medicine man from the mountains near Keetoowah, that old town from which in the ancient times the Cherokees had come, said, "I can write down the formulas now. All that I know will be kept forever."

"When we go home," promised the young men, "we will teach this in our towns."

"Teach it to everybody you meet," urged the chieftains, crowding about Sequoya to shake his hand, to pat his back, to tell him what a great thing he had done. The Lame One remembered that day. He remembered much of what was said. But most of all he remembered seeing Charley Hicks copying down the Cherokee pictures with great care, while a young man beside him wrote them first and repeated the sounds. He saw the pride too with which Agi-li showed everyone the letter he had brought with him, the letter from his son across the Mississippi written in Cherokee.

He heard Agi-li reminding Charley Hicks that in the old days when the messengers of the Iroquois had brought the wampum belt from the north they had said that the Cherokees were placed near the center of the sun; and that the talk therefore which was left for them was for all the Indian tribes, and when the Cherokees gave that talk, the voice of the Indians would be loud enough to be heard all over the land. "Now," said Agi-li, "the talking leaves of Sequoya are loud enough to bring me word from my son across the Mississippi!"

That day there was no stake set in the ground, no high-piled faggots to burn Sequoya as a witch. Instead there was a great feast. Sequoya sat beside Pathkiller. The whole council did him honor.

Then Sequoya and Ah-yo-ka went home to Sally. On the way he told Ah-yo-ka the story of the Flying Squirrel and the Bat. Ah-yo-ka clapped her hands with delight when she understood about the wings for the Flying Squirrel. But Sequoya said that was no longer important. What was important was that the ball be carried swiftly. All the Cherokees must learn. He himself would teach all he could. For the rest he must trust the young men.

He need not have been concerned. Because this was Indian knowledge, the Cherokees received it eagerly. The Nation was filled almost at once with people writing, with sticks in the dirt, with a stone on a boulder, cutting the Cherokee characters into the trees. Soon it was a common thing for letters to be sent from one town to another. No one went anywhere but he carried written messages in Cherokee to someone along the trail. In three months most of the Eastern Cherokees could read and write the new language which Sequoya had given them, the language of the talking leaves.

Sequoya was pleased at what had happened. The Birds had new help. But the Game of the whitemen against the Indians was well on its way to an ending in the east. The future of his people, Sequoya felt, must be in the west. He knew the ways of the white hunters only too well.

He remained a year in the east, teaching all those who came to him. The next year, he took his family and left once again for the land across the Mississippi. This time he carried many letters to the Western Cherokees, letters which would serve to renew old bonds between the two groups — talk to be heard over the land.

XII

The Game Goes On

(1828–1832)

SEQUOYA was on his way to Washington City with seven other delegates of the Western Cherokees. As he journeyed he wished more than once for Charley Hicks. Charley had been at the whiteman's capital many times — in his youth as an interpreter, and in later years for Pathkiller. He would have an idea what one might expect there.

But wishing for Charley was useless. Sequoya had lived with the Western Cherokees six years. He had word by letter that the other lame one, in the game of the strong against the weak, of the whitemen against the Indians, had died the year before. During the last year of his life Charley Hicks had served the Nation in the east as Principal Chieftain.

Lacking Charley's help, Sequoya did the next best thing. In quietness he gained strength to keep every sense alert, as one does who is about to travel an unknown trail lying in enemy country.

The little delegation from across the Mississippi was being

sent east to attempt to solve some of the difficulties the tribe was meeting in the new land. For one thing, the boundaries of the Cherokee possessions there had never been surveyed. Then, too, the tribe had been promised a perpetual outlet to the west, for as far as the soil rights of the Government should reach. Nothing at all had been done about that. Washington was very forgetful where Indians were concerned.

The delegation was instructed to bring to the officials' attention the fact that the Osages were continually making trouble, and the white settlers were crowding in. But they were warned that whatever the group did, they must not sell or exchange a single foot of tribal land. Only the chieftains in council could make treaties concerning land. A perpetual law had been passed in the Western Land to this effect, and the delegation might not even discuss that question.

John Jolly was the Principal Chieftain there now, and in pointing out the different matters which were to be brought up, he had emphasized this restriction again and again. The other matters, when Jolly talked them over, had seemed, before the group departed, fairly easy to handle. But the nearer they drew to Washington, the greater their undertaking loomed, the lower fell their spirits.

When once they were in the eastern city their spirits were low indeed. In spite of their most zealous efforts, it looked as though they might not be able to accomplish anything, that no single difficulty would be corrected, or that the whitemen would even admit there were difficulties.

After every brief interview they managed, the answer was that other matters were more pressing. The Cherokees should wait.

Wait? What were they waiting for? The Western Cherokees did not know. Some advised returning home at once, but others decided this would be foolish. After all the Government must expect to do something or they would not be given the advice to wait.

With every passing week, however, their bewilderment increased. Still it was a strange world into which they had come, and it was old wisdom that when one was at a loss as to what to do, it was better to do nothing. So Black Fox, Sequoya and the half-dozen others settled themselves in a hotel on Pennsylvania Avenue, held their councils there, and waited.

At first no one in Washington paid attention to them. Except for Sequoya the delegation wore whitemen's clothes. Sequoya was too proud to do that. He donned his hunting-shirt tunic, his leggings and moccasins and wound his turban about his head. Yet hardly anyone gave him a second glance. Indians, pleading for this or that favor, as the whitemen termed it, were common enough in Washington.

Then suddenly the indifference toward the little group was gone. Instead the Cherokees became the center of attention. They were besieged with visitors who asked impertinent questions and stared at all of them, but especially at Sequoya. One would have thought the besiegers had never seen such a person.

As a matter of fact, they hadn't. Washingtonians had just

learned that this American half-breed was responsible for a tremendous accomplishment. Even the papers which told about that accomplishment were at a loss for words to explain how great it really was. Why, this man had invented an alphabet — as the whitemen called the Cherokee syllabary — so simple, so adapted to the Cherokee language, that certain individuals had learned it in from one to three weeks, while almost the entire Cherokee Nation had acquired the ability to read and write in a matter of three months. Think of it! In that length of time the tribe had changed from an illiterate into a literate nation! Yet when he began his task, the man who had made this transition possible did not know even the rudiments of reading and writing!

To understand how astonishing it was, one had to realize that alphabets and syllabaries had hitherto been evolved only after centuries of study and experiment by many people, sometimes by many nations. Our own alphabet had come to us, for instance, by way of Egypt, Phoenicia and Greece and had taken centuries to produce. To be sure it was the best alphabet in the world, but this Cherokee's discovery was second best! And it had taken him merely a matter of ten years to produce, while he had given military service to the country during that period, and taken a long journey to the west as well.

There couldn't be argument as to the efficiency of the Cherokee writing. The missionaries among the Indians were responsible for the fact that a press was ready and a newspaper was to be issued using, in part, type with Sequoya's characters. It would be the very first Indian newspaper on this continent. A nephew of The Ridge was to be the editor.

The first issue of the *Cherokee Phoenix* came off the press while Sequoya and the other delegates were in Washington. While the name in some ways was not particularly fitting for an Indian newspaper, nevertheless it looked for a time as though it might be prophetic. Perhaps the Cherokee Nation, which had seemed on the way to certain destruction, would rise, as the fabled phoenix had done, from its very ashes.

At any rate many people at once became aware of what an intelligent, adaptable tribe the Cherokees really were. The Eastern Cherokees had reorganized their government, so that it was much like that of the whiteman. Their Principal Chieftain was chosen by election. They had two houses of government — the National Committee and the Council. The *Cherokee Phoenix* was printing reports as to their laws, their amazing progress in education, religion and the arts of civilized life.

In the midst of this excitement at the capital, the man who had made that Indian newspaper possible thought to himself how differently it had turned out from the days when he believed that the talking leaves would best serve his people by preserving the old wisdom. He still felt this was important, but his years of being alone had increased his ability to understand the Indians' problems. So he realized that it was even more necessary at this time to spread the whiteman's wisdom and the whiteman's ways among the Principal People. Kaluna, the adopted son of John Jolly — who had, after all, recovered from his wounds received at the Battle of Horseshoe Bend — must have realized this when he said that the gift of Sequoya was worth a bag of gold to every Cherokee.

There was an artist in Washington — Charles Bird King — who begged permission to paint Sequoya's picture. He would be proud, he said, to sign his name to a portrait of a man who had accomplished so much.

This conversation brought back the memory of Charley Hicks again — Charley, who had told him of the missionary at Tellico drawing the chieftains' pictures on a piece of paper and signing his name to each one; Charley, who had written down the name of Sequoya's father in the whiteman's manner.

Sequoya nodded his head as a sign that he was willing to have the portrait done. So, while with the rest of the delegation he waited for some further word from the Government, he sat hour after hour as the artist worked. A copy of the Cherokee sound-characters was in his hand, but after he had satisfied his curiosity as to the artist's methods, his eyes looked into the distance and saw many things. Once or twice before leaving the room he took the palette and brush and mixed the colors as he had seen the artist do. With the brush he outlined animals and human beings. The pictures were full of action and grace.

Then, when the portrait was completed, and when the patience of the Cherokees was near an end, they received a letter from the Secretary of War. It suggested that the group open negotiations for an exchange of land for the Western Cherokees. The new land was to be beyond the Arkansas Territory where the band was now located, and the negotiations, if concluded, would necessitate all the Cherokees in that area moving again.

The letter was a thunderbolt. To deal with a land question was the very thing the delegation could not do! They would not dare do it and go home and face the council. And to exchange, on their responsibility, all the western area, would result in their not even being allowed to explain — anything! Such an action would mean death for every one of them.

For once the quietness of the Cherokees was changed into volubleness; their gestures too were quick and as sharp as their words. But the Secretary of War did not appear the least impressed with their protests. Their quoting of the "perpetual law" of the Western Cherokees fell upon closed ears.

Instead the Secretary insisted that if the Cherokee delegation desired to serve their tribe, they must begin the land negotiations immediately. He understood, for instance, that the Cherokees wanted an outlet to the west. Well, they could have that outlet if they would make the land exchange. They had eight million acres where they now were. But just beyond they could have almost that amount — in much better country of course, free of white intruders and of unfriendly Indians. Also, if they moved to this new land, the Government was prepared to make immediate surveys. Consider what this meant — new unused land, filled with game, and an outlet running as far west as the soil rights of the country went — why, that outlet should amount to at least seven million acres more. This was more than a good exchange! It was an unparalleled opportunity!

Moreover this new land including the outlet would be guaranteed to them forever. It would even be named Indian Territory, while all white residents or "other objectionable people" would be removed immediately.

Forever was an easy word for whitemen to say. It had been included in every Indian treaty, since the beginning of treaties. The Indians had learned that it held little meaning. There was no lure in that word any longer, though the whitemen evidently thought it a sweet morsel hanging over their trap.

But the delegation fully realized that the trap must be there. They could sense the feeling in the air of the office where, after their first excited protest, they huddled in astounded silence. There was a set to their lips before the whitemen spoke to them, a snap to their words. After that first outburst the Cherokees held back their own words until they were in council alone.

The whitemen did not allow them to be alone long. There was meeting after meeting, argument after argument. The whitemen must have the Arkansas land. If the Indians refused to give it up freely, then much of what they held would be taken from them anyhow, and they would be in no position, as they were now, to bargain.

The President it seemed was in a mood to be generous. A little later might not find him so minded. Think of obtaining all the new acreage! Why, there would be plenty of room for the Cherokees from the east, when they should join their western countrymen. There seemed a certainty in the whitemen's minds that the Eastern Cherokees would join them.

It was all very confusing. The group dared not make the decision. They had no authority. And yet, if they did not do as the whitemen said, they feared they were indeed failing the Principal People.

They wavered. After all Sequoya was a good friend of John Jolly. Sequoya could explain to the Principal Chieftain just what had taken place, just why they had signed.

The whitemen were watching closely. The set of their lips changed. They smiled and bowed. Their words came now sweet as water in which pods of the honey locust are soaked. They urged the Indians to request anything they wanted. They themselves made suggestions.

Money for schools? Certainly. Money for a press so the Cherokees in the west could have a newspaper as well as their eastern brethren? Of course!

And how about five hundred dollars to Sequoya for the services he had rendered the Nation with his alphabet? They would put that in the treaty. And twelve hundred for Thomas Graves, who had, they remembered, sustained great losses of live-stock in the west, stolen perhaps by whitemen. Captain James Rogers, the interpreter, should certainly have five hundred for property losses and services rendered. What those services were the whitemen did not say.

There were other provisions, all apparently favorable to the signers or to the Cherokee Nation. By the time the treaty was ready it is doubtful whether the delegates knew what had been set down and what had been talked about. Of one thing however they were certain. They were giving away the Western Land. For the good of the tribe they were doing what they had been told not to do. If, after hearing their report, the council chose to enforce the law which called for their lives, then the law must be enforced! More important than what happened to them was the welfare of the Nation!

With heavy hearts they made ready to sign. Black Fox and Thomas Graves signed first with the sign of the crossed sticks. Then Sequoya took the pen. Swiftly he wrote his name — Sequoya — in Cherokee!

+ Geo: Guess

Then Thomas Maw, George Marvis and John Looney set down their names in Cherokee.

+ Thos maw

+ Geo. Marvis

+ John Looney

In his syllabary, Sequoya often uses two sounds for S when it comes at the beginning of a word.

Some official wrote "George Guess, Thomas Maw, George Marvis and John Looney" after the signatures, not knowing perhaps that those signatures were the signers' Cherokee names — Sequoya, Saniguya, Danosuli, Ugisudi. John Rogers was the only one who wrote in the whiteman fashion as the missionaries had taught him.

Sequoya, before he had left home, had anticipated signing his name in Cherokee writing. As it was, there was no pleasure at all, for him, or for others. Instead, after they had finished, the signers looked at one another as though each wondered how the others had managed to go through with the matter.

The whitemen soothed them. Doubtless the Senate would never ratify such a treaty. After all it was more than favorable to the Indians. They could hardly hope for such generous treatment as the signed paper called for. There was no need to be concerned, really.

Whitemen's words were smooth as water. They covered jagged rocks beneath.

For the treaty was ratified and that speedily. The whitemen presented a second paper. There was nothing for the Cherokees to do now, the whitemen said, but to put their crosses down. That would show they had accepted the treaty. They had made an astonishingly good bargain for the Western Cherokees. They were to be congratulated.

The Secretary of War himself would write a letter for them to carry back to the west, telling the others there exactly what had happened. The letter would report the good conduct and zeal of those who had carried through this difficult matter. In signing the treaty they had conferred immense benefits upon the tribe, the best possible thing had been done.

A white finger pointed to a spot on the paper, and pair after pair of bronzed fingers stiffly drew the cross. Why write in Cherokee now? Heartsick the delegation left the office, packed their meager belongings and started west.

On the way Sequoya's head whirled as he tried to remember how the treaty signing had come about, so as to tell John Jolly and the others in council just what had happened. But instead of the happenings of the past few months the thought of Doublehead kept returning to torment him, and the memory of The Ridge, who had, at the council's bidding, slain the traitor. Now that he was away from Washington City, Sequoya could see the matter of the treaty signing more and more from the tribe's viewpoint. In spite of the letter from the Secretary of War, he feared the worst.

He thought regretfully of the visit he had hoped to make to the Eastern Cherokees. After what had happened he did not want to go back to the places he had known in his youth. His increasing sense of uncertainty as to the wisdom of what the delegation had done would not have permitted that journey. Besides, now he must return to the west and plead, not merely for himself, but for the others.

If only what they had done should turn out — as the whitemen so often had declared it would — to be for the welfare of the tribe! Then he and his companions would be forgiven for what they had done. Only in the matter of intention was there a difference — if there was a difference — between himself and Doublehead!

The fears of Sequoya and those of his companions proved

well justified. The Western Cherokees, who had been ten years in the land, were furious when they heard that they would have to move on because of what the delegation had done.

There was loud talking in the council. The property of those who had gone to Washington was stolen. Their houses were burned in the night. Their livestock disappeared. There were threats against their lives. The council declared they were guilty of fraud and deception.

John Jolly however was willing to listen to Sequoya. The two faced each other squarely, and at last Jolly said simply, "I understand."

So, with Sequoya's pleading and Jolly's backing, the sentence of death was not passed. And though the hotbloods murmured among themselves, they did not dare go against the council.

Again and again Sequoya went over in detail what had taken place. Although the ears of the Western Cherokees heard his words, most did not accept them in their hearts until after the move was made, and they found themselves in land which was better than that which they had left. The Osages ceased to bother them. There were almost no whitemen in the area, and game was far more plentiful. Little by little ill feeling began to disappear, until it was admitted that the delegation to Washington had bargained well.

The Cherokees found many Creeks in the land to the south of them and more were coming in. It seemed familiar to have the Creeks to the south.

On the west side of Skin Bayou in the new Indian Territory,

Sequoya fashioned a cabin of logs. There was land for raising corn and beans. In time there were a few cattle, some oxen, and pigs. It wasn't so different from what it had been in the old days on the Tennessee.

When Sally's voice grew too insistent and the larder ran low, the Lame One yoked the oxen to an old cart, filled it with tools, camping equipment and food and moved northward through the woods to his salt lick. This was a dozen or more miles from the cabin. Here he could have the quiet to which he had become accustomed. He would often remain many weeks making salt. He scooped the water out of the spring, boiled it in a great kettle until the water evaporated, scraped out the deposit and began all over again.

Now and then some Cherokee came to him there to be taught to read and write. Sequoya was always willing to stop his work and teach the Cherokee characters. He was glad too when someone asked for the old wisdom, formulas for hunting, or healing, and for the old stories.

He went occasionally to a nearby mission school, not to learn of the whiteman's God, but for copies of the *Cherokee Phoenix,* which came from the east.

In spite of their promise to the Western Cherokees, and in spite of the fact that these were included in the treaty, the Government had not provided money for the press or the schools in the west. Other things they had promised had not, for the most part, been taken care of either. But the Cherokees had moved as they agreed, and the new land had been surveyed by the

Government fairly promptly. Perhaps that was as much as the Indians could expect from the whitemen.

Something important had gone out of Sequoya's life when he returned from the east. In spite of his acceptance once more among the Western Cherokees, there was a feeling in himself that he had failed the Principal People. It was as though in the ball game, he had dropped the ball and the other side had seized it. He did not know what he should do.

And then, four years after his winter in Washington City, there was a knock at his cabin door. The Cherokee, Charley Vann, from the east was standing there, holding a letter and a package in his hand; the latter he handed to Sequoya. It was, he announced, from John Ross, Head of Council, Cherokee Nation.

Sequoya wondered why Ross was sending him a letter, but Charley Vann was translating it aloud:

Head of Coosa, Cherokee Nation, January 12, 1832.

"My friend:

The legislative Council of the Cherokee Nation in the year 1824 voted a medal to be presented to you, as a token of respect and admiration for your ingenuity in the invention of the Cherokee alphabetical characters —"

Sequoya lifted his head and drew a quick breath.

"and in pursuance thereof, the two late venerable Chiefs, Path Killer and Charles R. Hicks, instructed a delegation of this Nation . . ."

It was Charley who had suggested it then! Of this the listener was sure. For years Pathkiller had done as his assistant suggested.

"composed of Messrs. George Lowry, Senior . . ."

Charley, the other lame one, and Agi-li had accomplished it! His old friends and all the Eastern Cherokees seemed suddenly very near to the listener. Until that moment he had not realized how lonely he had been for them.

"Elijah Hicks and myself . . ."

Elijah! That was Charley's son.

"to have one struck, which was completed in 1825. In the anticipation of your visit to this country, it was reserved for the purpose of honoring you with its presentment by the Chiefs in General Council;"

They would have honored him at a great council! All the Chiefs! But, he couldn't have accepted it, not after that winter in Washington. It was well he had not returned to the Eastern Cherokees then.

"but having been so long disappointed in this pleasing hope, I have thought it my duty no longer to delay, and therefore taken upon myself the pleasure of delivering it, through our friend, Mr. Charles H. Vann, who intends visiting his relatives in the country where you dwell. In receiving this small tribute from the representatives of the people of your Native Land, in the honor of your transcendant invention, you will, I trust, place a

proper estimate on the grateful feeling of your fellow country-men. The beginning, the progress, and the final completion of the grand scheme, is full evidence that the efforts of all the powers of man of more than ordinary genius were put in action. The present generation have already experienced the great benefits of your incomparable system. The old and the young find no difficulty in learning to read and write in their Native language and to correspond with their distant friends with the same facility as the Whites do. Types have been made and a printing press established in this nation. The scriptures have been translated and printed in Cherokee;"

Sequoya nodded. He had been told of that, time enough, by the missionaries when he went for the *Phoenix*. Agi-li's son-in-law had done it, and Agi-li, that great orator, had helped him. After that work Agi-li had turned to the whiteman's god. But in the eastern mountains near the ancient town of Keetoowah, Sequoya knew the old men had started setting down their formulas in his writing. All the gods, both those of the whiteman and the Indian, were making use of the Cherokee characters!

"and whilst posterity continues to be benefited by the discovery, your name will exist in grateful remembrance. It will also serve as an index for other aboriginal tribes, or nations, similarly to advance in science and respectability; in short, the great good designed by the author of human existence in directing your genius in this happy discovery, cannot be fully estimated — it is incalculable." *

* Quoted from the Payne Mss., Courtesy of Newberry Library, Chicago.

Sequoya opened the package then. The large medal was of silver. In both English and Cherokee it said: *Presented to George Gist * by the General Council of the Cherokee Nation.* Under the inscription were two crossed pipes. There was a head on the reverse side, a likeness, Charles Vann explained, of Sequoya.

The recipient's heart leaped. The head— a picture of him! That marked the medal again as Charley Hicks' idea. "Do you remember," the medal seemed to say, "when we talked of these matters and I wrote down your name for you?"

Charley was dead. But here he was speaking to him through the medal. It was as though Charley knew at last of Sequoya's feeling concerning the ancient story of the ball game and its relation to the present struggle of the strong against the weak. With that medal Charley Hicks was passing the ball on to him for his carrying.

He fingered the two crossed pipes thoughtfully. They stood, he knew, for the Eastern and Western Cherokees.

* The white name of Sequoya sometimes spelled thus.

XIII

This Is What Happened . . .

(. . . 1839)

"THIS IS WHAT happened in the old days when the Cherokees lived in the Eastern Land." After 1838 that was the way the Cherokee storytellers always began their tales. This is the story Sequoya, the Lame One, heard. As he listened he kept his fingers pressed upon the two crossed pipes on the medal which hung about his neck:

"In Georgia, matters grew steadily worse for our people. And all the while we saw what was happening to the Creeks.

"Do you remember William McIntosh, who led the friendly Creeks under Andrew Jackson at the Battle of Horseshoe Bend? Well, McIntosh accepted a bribe to sell some more Creek land, and even dared appear at one of our councils with a letter for John Ross. That letter promised Ross and Charley Hicks and others of our chieftains large sums if they would sign treaties selling the Cherokee Land.

"Ross read the letter aloud and denounced the man and his offer. He called him a traitor, worse than the meanest snake that crawls the earth; while The Ridge declared he should be cast behind his back, since he was bought with money. McIntosh barely escaped from that council. And when the Creeks realized that he had accepted bribes and ceded Creek lands in Georgia, they killed him according to their law.

"But it was too late to save the tribe. The Creeks, those once proud warriors, were a broken people, divided among themselves. They were driven from their homes and hunted like mad dogs. Some of them fled for shelter among us and we received them — after all, they had been our neighbors for a long time — but the whites ferreted them out. The whites declared they were barbarians. When they said the word, they looked at us with hatred in their eyes, and we knew that in their hearts they were thinking the same thing of us. We felt that when the Creeks were gone, then our turn would come.

"So our chieftains declared we must show ourselves as civilized as the whitemen. We must take the path they had traveled and walk in the same fashion.

"We did take that path. We fashioned our constitution. Our officers were elected. Charley Hicks was our first elected Principal Chieftain. After he died many wanted the chieftain of Willstown in his place. But George Lowry — Agi-li — declared that one was needed who knew the ways of the whitemen better than he; so we chose John Ross, the friend of The Ridge. Agi-li became his assistant.

"Not a Cherokee but knew why we were taking the white man's way. In Cherokee writing we sent word to the farthest town, the most lonely cabin. We had our newspaper too, in our language and the whiteman's language as well, and it went to everyone who could read. With their writing had the whitemen tricked us. But now we too had talking leaves for our using.

"We divided our land into districts and had our law officers, our judges and courts. Our laws were put down in the Cherokee writing, so everyone understood them. Our capital where our general councils were held was near Oostanaula. We called it New Echota, in memory of the Peace Town on the Tennessee. There was strength in the name.

"Many of our young men had been trained in the whitemen's schools and they helped us do all these things. We encouraged new schools and welcomed new teachers among us. The white missionaries who came were our friends. There was one whom we named A-tse-nu-sti, the Messenger.* His white name was Samuel Worcester. He helped us obtain our press on which we printed our newspaper and so many books in Cherokee. We set down the missionaries' Book too in Cherokee writing, and even before the new press was ready, we passed the manuscript from hand to hand.

"The whitemen in Georgia watched us and knew they could

* At Brainerd Mission, Tenn., 1817, then at New Echota, Ga.

no longer call us barbarians and get rid of us because we were ignorant. So they planned a new trap. They declared that only the whiteman's law should prevail over their land and ours. We were forbidden to meet in councils any more to choose our own officers. We were not to enforce our own laws. But neither could we have the protection of the whiteman's law. We could not testify in his courts, not even in our own defense. Whitemen stole our property, they murdered our people. And we could do nothing.

"We knew they were doing these things because they were trying to force us from the land we had possessed before the whitemen came across the ocean. We were not allowed to continue as a separate Nation. Neither could we become citizens of Georgia. Once we had been told that such citizenship was open to us. Now even that was denied.

"We were less than the wind that blew over our mountain peaks. And sometimes we possessed no more than the wind possessed. We dug roots and ate leaves for food. Many of us were becoming as destitute as the Creeks. But we stood together with The Ridge and John Ross who kept bidding us to hold fast.

"The whitemen were determined it should be otherwise. 'You must leave,' they kept saying. 'You must leave.' Then gold was discovered in our land, and the whitemen went wild.

"They laid out new counties where our lands extended. They divided our property and drew lots as to which whiteman should have which piece of our ground. They stole our cattle and horses. They drove us from our own houses and took them for themselves. There was nothing we could do.

"While these things were happening, The Ridge and John Ross still stood together and encouraged us to endure. The Ridge was not educated as Ross was educated, in the whiteman's fashion, but he had the wisdom and judgment of the fullblood. Finally The Ridge declared there was no use trying to continue. In the end, he said, we would be broken and destroyed as the Creeks were being destroyed.

"The Ridge said it would be better to leave and to save the Principal People. We should yield and join our tribesmen beyond the Great River. The Nation must be united.

"But Ross said, no, we should hang on. If the whitemen did succeed in driving us out, we should leave this country altogether. What good would it do us to go beyond the Mississippi, he demanded, when our people there had already been forced to move once? As long as the Indian dwelt with the whitemen in this land, the whitemen would keep saying, 'This is mine! Move on!'

" 'It is not the truth they speak, when they say this,' declared Ross. 'The land in Georgia is ours. It has been since our father's father's time. Let us be patient, no matter what happens. We have some friends in Washington. In the end we shall receive justice.'

"Because The Ridge and the Principal Chieftain now saw things differently they grew to distrust each other. The Government in Georgia seized our press, so there was no way we could learn the truth.

"A new President of the United States was elected. It was Andrew Jackson — the Chicken Snake. We understood now that he had hated and tricked us for a long time. He had traded upon our trust and friendship. Now he declared all the Indians must go beyond the Mississippi. There was a bill passed in Congress to remove all of the Eastern Tribes.*

"The Ridge went to Washington City with his son and his nephew and made a long talk. And the Principal Chieftain went to Washington and he talked.

"But The Ridge would agree to the removal now, so the white-men paid attention to him. The Ridge came back and a council meeting at New Echota in Georgia was called. The whitemen allowed us to have it, for they wanted the Cherokees to sign a treaty there. But the Principal Chieftain sent word through the Nation that the people were not to attend.

"About a fourth of the people went. For there were those who believed as The Ridge did, that it was useless to struggle any longer. At New Echota a treaty was signed, giving up all the Eastern Cherokee Land.

"The Ridge signed that treaty and his son and his nephew —

* The Choctaws, Chickasaws and Seminoles were removed, in addition to the Cherokees and Creeks. In 1828, Georgia; 1829, Alabama; 1830, Mississippi; 1835, Tennessee, passed laws extending the jurisdiction of these several states over the Indian lands within their borders. Of course there were individuals in all these places who sympathized with the Indians, and wanted them to receive justice, but these were helpless.

the one who had edited the Cherokee newspaper. These three were the leaders now against Ross, the Principal Chieftain.

"When The Ridge signed that treaty at New Echota his face was very sober. For he was the one who had made it a written law in the council that whoever signed away Cherokee Land should die. He did this after McIntosh had signed away some of the Creek land. We did not need that law, for we had always known that the land was the tribe's and not the individual's. We remembered the traitor, Doublehead. But on that day when The Ridge signed the treaty giving up the Eastern Land, there were those who heard him say afterward: 'I have signed for my death.'

"Some say The Ridge was a traitor. And others declare he did a brave thing, that he thought only of saving the Nation from the stubbornness of Ross. These maintain that The Ridge had more years behind him on the trail of his life, so he saw more clearly into the future, while others think he was ambitious for himself and his son.

"It is difficult to know which are the true words. Most of the things which were said of The Ridge were said, by others, of Ross. Still it must be remembered that Ross was the Principal Chieftain. We could not have elections at New Echota, our capital, for the whitemen would not permit it, so Ross had continued to serve us. Because he was the leader, we must trust him. He had borne himself well and outwitted the whitemen many times.

"Yet the dullest of us could see that the remnant of our neighbors, the Creeks, were being moved westward. In chains and manacles, many of those who had endured great persecution in Georgia were being driven out now like wild horses. In the winter they went with no covering for their feet, with only cotton clothing for the women. Many died on the way. Some who escaped reported that the trail could be followed by the scattering of human bones.

"After the Treaty of New Echota, The Ridge and many others went from us to the Cherokees beyond the Mississippi. Though before he went, The Ridge did his best to mitigate our sufferings — that we know. And some of the missionaries began to go west then. Springplace had been seized by the whitemen. Two missionaries had been put in prison for a long time because they stood by us. One of them was A-tse-nu-sti, our friend. He, who had suffered for us, said that it was better for us to leave.

"John Ross was furious when he knew about the treaty. He sent a paper through the Nation and it was signed by thousands. That paper protested the treaty and declared it was not our will. Ross was our Principal Chieftain. We did, as we had done so long, just what he advised.

"At Washington it was said that the treaty at New Echota had been made openly and in the public square. There were many statesmen who took our side. But in the end the treaty was ratified by only one more vote than was needed.

"So officials at Washington set the time for our going. They were giving us five million for our land in the east. But our gold mines, our chieftain said, were worth more than that.

"There is an old, old tale among the Cherokees, as you know. It tells that the whitemen who first came among us were seeking for gold. Some of our people say it was the discovery of gold which was our ruin. But others think it was the whiteman's craze for land.

"We could not believe that we would be driven out, not even after Washington set the time. And when John Ross managed to have that time extended for two years, we told ourselves he was clever and would find a way so we would not leave at all.

"We had to have trust in something, so we trusted in him. He was driven from his great house in Georgia and lived in a one-room cabin in Tennessee. He kept fighting on.

"The Chief Justice of the Supreme Court in Washington, he told us, a man named Marshall, had declared that we had rights and that Georgia should respect them. But we heard too that Chicken Snake had said, 'Marshall has given his decision. Now let him enforce it.' The President himself would do nothing. And we learned next that the government of Georgia was more powerful than the Supreme Court of the United States.

"This is how we learned it. On a day when we did not expect it the white soldiers appeared. They came to the doors of our homes with their guns drawn and said we must come with them.

"They did not give us time to milk the cows or feed the chickens. They stopped whatever we were doing and ordered us into line with the points of their bayonets. If a woman wanted to gather things she needed, she was prodded roughly and put with the others. There was one little girl who seized her pet duck and hugged it close. It was the only thing she carried away with her.

"We looked over our shoulders and saw whitemen taking or destroying what we had just left. It is a hard thing to see. Whitemen were even opening graves to tear the silver ornaments from our dead. Many a Cherokee home was burning as we were marched past. To all of our towns, they came; and to every cabin in the mountains or the valleys.

"But what followed after was harder still. For we were put in camps with high walls around them. We were like so many beasts crowded together to be slaughtered. We were guarded with guns, so we could not escape.

"Many of us had been hunters. All of us had been free.

"We were free no longer. We were caged. We were fed little food, and often it was not fit to eat. We had musty corn-meal or whitemen's flour with creeping things in it, and meat which was old and rancid. We were not accustomed to such fare and it made us ill. The whitemen laughed at our distress. They would not even allow the women to go out and gather some of the wild roots and leaves, medicines that would have helped us.

"Only a few of our jailers were sorry and did what they could for us. We were months in those pens. Some of the fortunate ones died then.

"John Ross saw what was happening, so he redoubled his efforts. He demanded that if we must be removed that he have charge of our going. And this was agreed to. It was also agreed that we might wait until the hot weather was over, so there would not be so much illness.

"The Principal Chieftain divided the people into groups. He put those of the same clan together. He put over each group a chieftain to whom we were accustomed. He used good judgment in those he chose. Two sons of Charley Hicks were among our leaders. George Lowry — Agi-li — gathered the wampum belts, the old treasures of the tribe, and we took these with us. Agi-li was the head of the Cherokee National Committee. When Ross was away, Agi-li acted in his absence.

"The groups began moving in the autumn. A few went by the rivers, but most of us journeyed by land. It was February before the last of us reached the land across the Mississippi. There were wagons and horses for some. But most walked the greater part of the way. We suffered from lack of food, and the last groups to leave the east had to change their route, for those who had gone before had killed off the game. Much of the way, as you know, was through unsettled country, and sometimes we waded through swamps up to our waists in water. We suffered new and strange diseases. And we, the Principal People, were afraid all the time!

"We were not ashamed of being afraid. The trail we were made to take was a hard one. We called it the Trail Where We Cried.

"Little things we remember make us sad still. There was the child with the duck. She had managed to keep it with her all during the time we were penned together. But one day on the trail her feet hurt her, so she began sobbing. In her agony she squeezed the duck too close and it became a limp thing in her arms. A soldier saw its head falling over the child's wrist, so he seized it and threw it aside. After that the little girl did not cry any more. She kept her tears forever in her heart.

"There were women who kept their tears thus when they buried their children beside the trail and left them alone and in a strange land. There were those who were thankful when some suffering one died because the dead did not have to follow the sorrowful trail any farther.

"There were seventeen thousand of us when the soldiers started gathering us into the pens. There were four thousand less when we arrived here in the west.

"Not one of us but has suffered much. Mostly the children and the old people died on the way, for the journey was too difficult for them. Our Principal Chieftain's wife was among those who died. But Ross put our suffering above his own. He did for us everything he could. We all suffered and worked for each other.

"Now when we lived in the Old Country in the east, and were trying to save our lands there, we moved swiftly along the whiteman's trail and learned his ways. Our leaders knew and we knew that we could follow the old trail of the Indian no longer.

"But now that we have come to the west, many of the Cherokees already here, it is clear, have not gone so swiftly nor so far along that new trail as we. Nor do they wish to travel the new trail. They choose instead to return to the old days and live by hunting and trapping. They are scornful of the whiteman's ways. They are few in number also, but they declare we, who are many, have come to them, and therefore we must accept their ways and live under their government.

"On our part we see only confusion among you in the west. There is no great chieftain. John Jolly is dead, and his assistant, we understand, has refused to take his place. We ask, where are your great chieftains? And where is your government? Why should we accept when you have so little to offer?

"We do not hear a clear answer. But we see many glance in the direction of The Ridge and his son, as though waiting a signal.

"We are the Principal People, we of the east. We have not come to the end of the journey to give up what little we have managed to keep. We are glad to see our relatives and our friends who are here. Yet we feel — we cannot help feeling — that if you who are here had not led the way in the old days, and gone from us across the Great River, the Government at Washington would not have had an excuse to send us after you.

"Can we help it that we are angry when we see The Ridge and his son and his nephew, and those who came with them, now prosperous and cared for? They were the ones who signed the treaty of New Echota. And that treaty in the end tricked us out of our land, out of everything we possessed. Our young men talk of this in whispers. We hear them. And we watch them fingering their knives.

"I am not telling you what is right and what is wrong. I am telling you what has come to pass.

"John Ross has served us long. He has fought and suffered and done for us. He is one of us. We will never give him up. Yet the word has gone round that The Ridge intends to put his son over us as Chieftain of all the Cherokees.

"Would that we had a spell such as our fathers knew in the old days when we lived in the east, a spell which would set things at rights for us all once more. But perhaps there is no spell. Perhaps the old men spoke truth when they said that for the Cherokees the west was the land of darkness and defeat."

The Lame One had pressed his fingers so hard upon the crossed pipes, that when he removed them, the imprint of the pipes remained a long time in his flesh.

XIV

Sequoya Works a Spell

(June–July 1839)

THE ANTAGONISM and suspicion between Eastern and Western Cherokees increased as the months passed. The Lame One saw what was happening. He listened to both sides and was heartsick. The Eastern Cherokees were fearful of the domination of the smaller groups; while the Western Cherokees declared that those from the east had come to enslave them. No one knew better than Sequoya how difficult it was to judge sometimes as to what was right and what was wrong. He talked with Ross and felt that the Eastern Cherokees' belief in their leader was well-founded. And he went over all the details which had built up his own, and the Western Cherokees' trust in The Ridge.

As for the treaty which The Ridge had signed, Sequoya had only to recall that he himself had signed a treaty in Washington City, for which he might well have paid with his life. More than one knife had been sharpened when he and his companions came home and told what they had done. Yet he knew the motives which had caused them to sign, and how in the end the welfare for the tribe had won out against their own fear.

He knew also — he had always known — how important it was to keep the Cherokee Nation united. He remembered the tale the old men had told him of the time when the Cherokees first began going westward — the story of the Lost Cherokees. These had always been missed from the tribe. He remembered how in his youth the Overhill Towns had missed the warriors who had left them, those who had been called the Chickamaugas.

The whitemen would succeed only too well in the game, if at the end of the long journey, the Cherokees should begin destroying one another. He felt that if he were going to do his part to avert this, he must move quickly. He squared his shoulders.

Because his mother's clan had always possessed strong influence over the Principal People, he knew he could depend upon great strength in whatever he undertook.

But the evil words which the two groups were spreading brought disaster faster than Sequoya could work his spell. For a long time no one knew all of what was happening. But this much soon became clear.

The young men from the east, who had been whispering and fingering their knives, called a council, secretly and at night. They did not tell Ross for they knew he would forbid it. But they talked at the council held in the nighttime of what The Ridge, his son and his nephew had done. The whiskey went round.

Loosened tongues repeated how in the old days The Ridge himself had gone forth at the bidding of the council to kill Doublehead, who had been a traitor to his people. They told too how The Ridge had said that the old custom must be made a law — that it should be put down in black and white that whoever should sell Cherokee land should die. And they told over and over about the treaty of New Echota, and emphasized that The Ridge, his son and his nephew were responsible for that.

Bird, the son of Doublehead, talked loudest of all. The young men drew closer together. Lots were drawn and orders given.

The next morning the son of The Ridge was attacked at his home and killed. The Ridge was set upon from ambush as he traveled a lonely road, and he was killed. His nephew was lured from his work with the white missionary — A-tse-nu-sti — and brutally slain.

Such were the breathless reports which came, one upon the other, to Sequoya. He was aghast. Was this then the end of the Cherokees? He could almost hear the Western Cherokees — the old settlers — declaring that John Ross had ordered the murders to be rid of his rivals. And he was equally certain that this was not true.

Yet such was the feeling between the two groups that a struggle to the death might easily develop. In this struggle, the still warlike tribes of the Indians about them would be only too glad to join.

There were good spells, he realized, and there were evil ones. The good spells worked more slowly than the evil. Though in the end the good spells were stronger.

Could he work a good spell now, with matters at this point? Could he?

The memory of Wurteh standing in the dawn at the mouth of the mountain cave came back to him; the memory of himself taking part in the races; the memory too of the old story of the Bat and the Ground Squirrel. His lips moved, but the Cherokees who had brought him news of the slayings did not hear what Sequoya said. They saw only that his shoulders straightened and his face grew calm.

The son of Wurteh of the Red Paint Clan began working his spell, the spell that one who had suffered and triumphed over suffering could work, the spell that a man could work who had faltered and lost the trust of his fellows, yet regained it again.

With the words he spoke day after day, he worked that spell; and with the letters he set down in his writing and sent through the Western Land. He reminded the old settlers that the Cherokee Nation must remain united always. He told them how Old Tassel had said that to work for the people and not for one's self was important. The newcomers were their relatives, their friends.

He spoke to the followers of The Ridge and told them how he too had been named traitor of his Nation because he had signed a treaty. In the end what he had done had worked for the good of the people. Now that was recognized. In time it would be known that The Ridge was not a traitor. He had done his best for the tribe.

John Ross had not known what his young men had planned. Of that Sequoya was more than certain. There were men who had been with Ross the whole time and could confirm his words.

Neither was Ross traitor; he too had worked according to what had seemed best to him. A mountain has more than one path. The land of their fathers in Georgia had indeed belonged to the Cherokees. Justice was on their side, but justice does not always prevail.

It would not aid the Cherokees to continue the fight against one another, to destroy the strongest among them. The white-men would destroy what was left. The Principal People would have failed Keetoowah.

" 'Let us get together,' he urged. 'We have all suffered. Out of that suffering now must come our strength.' "

At a camp ground in a valley, Sequoya and John Ross summoned the people, Western and Eastern Cherokees together.

At first the Western Cherokees would not come. They sent word they were fearful of being murdered as The Ridge and his relatives had been. They had heard, they declared, that liquor was being passed about, and rumor had it that the young men who had done the bloody deeds had fortified themselves for the task with the whiteman's drink. It was these same young men, the old settlers among the Cherokees insisted, who were present at the meeting to which they were summoned. They were not going to be foolish enough to come into the midst of their enemies.

Sequoya had agreed to act as President for the Western Cherokees, and to preside over the meeting. So, as the words of explanation reached him as to why the Western Cherokees would not come, he sent out a letter to his friends. In the characters of his talking leaves he set the words down:

"We, the old settlers, are here in council with the late emigrants, and we want you to come up without delay, that we may talk matters over like friends and brothers. These people are here in great multitudes, and they are perfectly friendly toward us. They have said, over and over again, that they will be glad to see you and we have full confidence that they will receive you with all friendship. There is no drinking here to disturb the peace though there are upwards of two thousand people on the ground. We send you these few lines as friends and we want you to come on without delay; and we have no doubt but we can have all things amicably and satisfactorily settled." *

The letter was one such as only Sequoya could write. He said what was needed. And numbers of the old settlers came. At the meeting Sequoya used many of the arts he had learned, that of the storyteller, the persuader; and the reasoning which had been strengthened during his years of work on his talking leaves. He used these arts deftly, powerfully.

He told of the old days when the Cherokees lived in the east. "Then," he said, "the rabbit dwelt in the broomsage of the hill-

* Foreman, Grant. *Sequoyah,* courtesy of University of Oklahoma Press.

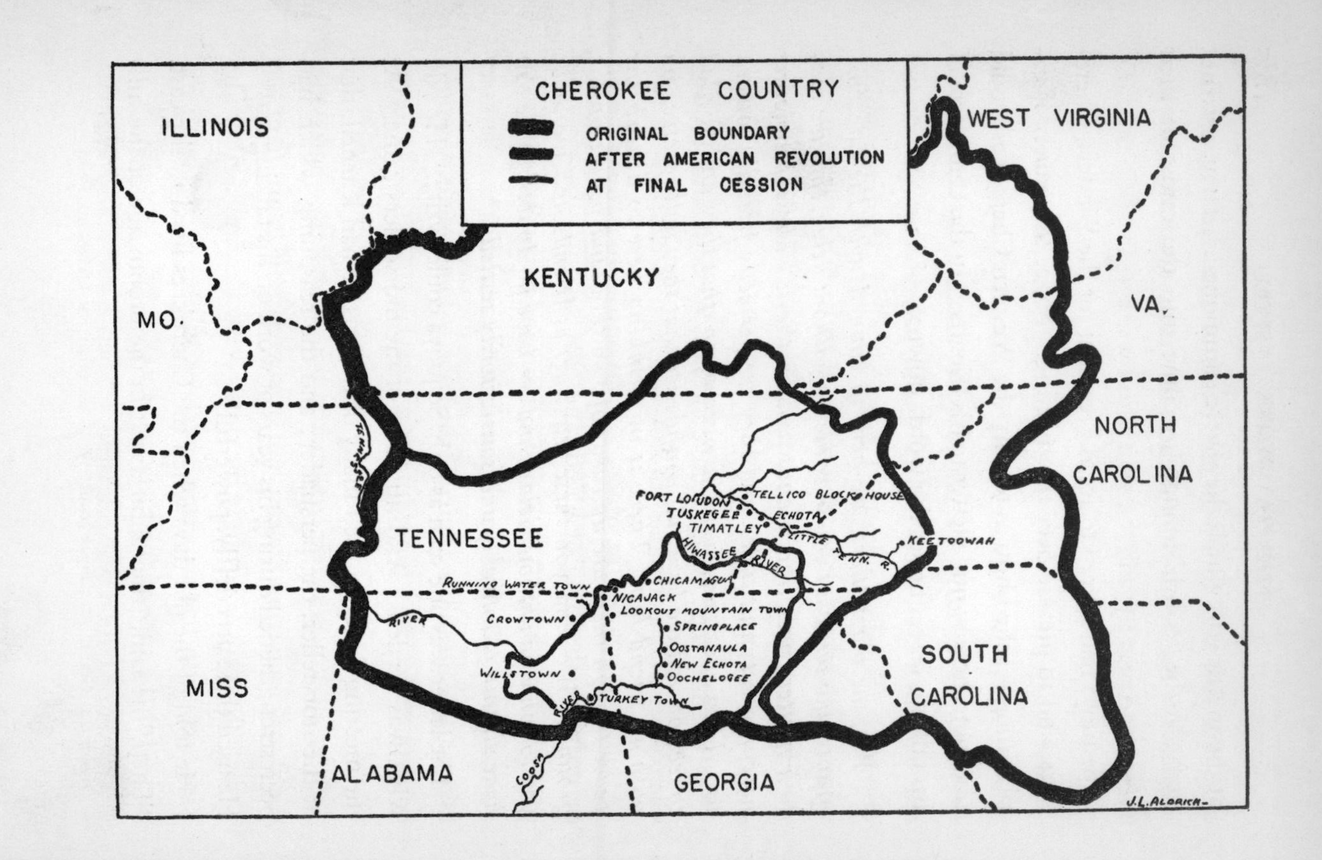
CHEROKEE COUNTRY
ORIGINAL BOUNDARY
AFTER AMERICAN REVOLUTION
AT FINAL CESSION
ILLINOIS
MO.
KENTUCKY
WEST VIRGINIA
VA.
NORTH CAROLINA
TENNESSEE
SOUTH CAROLINA
MISS
ALABAMA
GEORGIA
FORT LOUDON
TELLICO BLOCK HOUSE
TUSKEGEE
ECHOTA
TIMATLEY
LITTLE TENN. R.
KEETOOWAH
HIWASSEE RIVER
RUNNING WATER TOWN
CHICAMAGUA
NICAJACK
LOOKOUT MOUNTAIN TOWN
CROWTOWN
SPRINGPLACE
OOSTANAULA
NEW ECHOTA
OOCHELOGEE
WILLSTOWN
TURKEY TOWN
RIVER
TENNESSEE
COOSA
J.L. ALDRICH

side, the fish was found in the bend of the river, under the shadows of the hemlock branches; the turtles were together in a great pond near by, and the whirlwind was ever on the mountain top.

"But when the fire swept the broomsage, the rabbit went elsewhere; when the river dried up, the fish were found to have departed. The turtles left one place for another; and there were seasons when even the whirlwind disappeared from the mountain tops. So was it with the Cherokees. Like the birds which migrate from one place to another, they had left the home of their fathers and had come to a new country. There they should dwell together in peace."

At last the spell was effective! Both Western and Eastern Cherokees were persuaded that it was fatal to continue as two factions, one against the other. It was agreed that there should be no more shedding of blood, and that a pardon be given to those who had killed The Ridge, his son and his nephew. After a time those who had participated in the slayings might even take part again in the affairs of the tribe. Their identity would be kept secret, and the whiteman's government should never know.

After all, it was recognized that in doing what they had done, the young men from the east had followed the old custom of the Tribe. Rightly or wrongly the deeds were accomplished. The Ridge, at least, had expected and been willing to pay with his life — for the sake of the Principal People.

An Act of Union was prepared. Then Eastern and Western

Cherokees in National Convention assembled, solemnly and mutually agreed to form themselves into one body, under the style and title of the Cherokee Nation. Everyone recognized that while this was not the end of the struggle between the two groups, it was a first step toward that end.

Agi-li signed that Act of Union as President of the Eastern Cherokees. Then Sequoya took up the pen to sign as President of the Western Cherokees.

There were many in the group who, as they watched the two men signing, thought of Old Tassel, the Beloved Chieftain of Old Echota. He had been known too as a Peacemaker.

Perhaps their thoughts came to the signers. For when Sequoya and Agi-li laid down their pens, for a long time they looked quietly into each other's eyes.

XV

Up the Last River

(1842–1843)

THE CHEROKEE NATION was one. John Ross was its chieftain. Since the word Echota was no longer a name beloved, the new capital of the Principal People was called Tahlequah. That was after the old town of Tellico on the Tennessee River. Tellico symbolized the days of greatness of the Nation in the east before the whitemen began crowding close.

There were many, however, who during the difficult years of readjustment between the Eastern and Western Cherokees had gone farther west. There was a group of them, it was reported, in Mexico. Perhaps, Sequoya thought, the Lost Cherokees, of whom the storytellers had told when he was young, were there too.

He decided he must go to these tribesmen, must teach them

the Cherokee writing, must, if possible, persuade them to return and join the Principal People. He would visit other tribes along the way. Perhaps he would be able to work out a writing which all the Indian tribes could use and understand — "talk to be heard over the land." He had already helped the Choctaw Nation to develop a written language.

There were those among the Cherokees who said he was old. He feared they would try to dissuade him. So he made his preparations secretly, and he swore to secrecy his son Teesy, and the handful of other companions he had chosen to go with him. He prepared an ox cart and filled it with much manuscript. He took with him the history he had been writing, the history of the Cherokee People. It was filled with accounts of all the old formulas and stories. He hoped to find more material to set down.

He said good-bye to Sally. Then he went to the home of his old friend, Archibald Campbell, who had been with him at the Battle of Horseshoe Bend. From there he and his companions set forth.

The journey was more difficult than he had anticipated. The ox cart was broken, mended, and broken again. Finally it was discarded. The tribes with whom Sequoya stayed on the way received him with kindness and urged him to remain with them.

But nothing would stop Sequoya. A sense of urgency drove him on. It was something such as he had felt in the old days when he had fled with Wurteh and the other Cherokees to the mountains; as he had sensed when he had first gone west to escape the hatred of the old men.

Sometimes he was able to obtain horses from the Indians. Sometimes he was forced to journey on foot. The accounts which have sifted back show hardship and suffering; they show also Sequoya's unalterable determination. They do not indicate too certainly what actually happened when he and his companions reached Mexico.

A long time afterward, however, word was received in the Cherokee Nation that Sequoya had died in Mexico among the Cherokees there, and that he was buried at San Fernando in the month of August, 1843. But of this no man is absolutely certain. The manuscripts he took with him have never been found.

The life which had begun in mystery had ended in mystery. Sequoya had fled up the last river. This time the hunter was Death, and his arrow was certain.

"Tsâ′ gĭ, tsâ′ gĭ, hwĭ′lahĭ,
Tsâ′ gĭ, tsâ′ gĭ, hwĭ′lahĭ."

ᏣᎩ ᏣᎩ ᏫᎳᎯ
ᏣᎩ ᏣᎩ ᏫᎳᎯ

On the Tennessee–North Carolina boundary line there is a mountain lifting high. It is named Sequoyah. In the State of Georgia there is a statue to its Cherokee son, and a marker where the building once stood which housed the first Indian press in the country. In Oklahoma, the Skin Bayou District where Sequoya built his log cabin, has been renamed Sequoyah County. The log cabin itself is preserved forever.

In the Capitol at Washington, the statue of Sequoya stands proudly in a great hall among the representations of other great men of our country. On the doors of the annex of the Congressional Library are representations in bas-relief of those who have contributed most to perfecting written languages — the alphabet-makers. Among them is the North American, Sequoya.

While in our westernmost state — California — are found great trees, the oldest living tree in the Western Hemisphere, the tallest and the most nearly immortal. These are Sequoias.

Sequoya! It was a name worn proudly. It is a good word to say.

Author's Word

THE STORY of Sequoya has never been written for young people. One reason may be that the reports concerning this half-breed Cherokee were told after his great discovery. They came by way of the interpreter and were frequently colored by the speaker as well as by the feelings of those who thought it worthwhile to record them. Also, such material as is in existence is scattered, difficult to obtain, and often contradictory.

Since the life of Sequoya can be properly told only against the background of his people, it has seemed permissible to choose from accounts concerning him that material which appears consistent with the man and the period; and to assume in some instances the effect of the period upon the individual concerned.

There is much that we do not know; either because there is no record at all, or because the available folklore may be contradictory. These unimportant details include such matters as the year of Sequoya's birth (which appears to me to be about 1770), the identity of his father, the name which his mother gave him, the exact incident which called his attention to the "talking leaves," the time and the number of his marriages, the exact place and the time of his death.

The dates during which he perfected his great discovery,

"worth a bag of gold in the hand of every Cherokee," are not in question; nor are the ways, times and places in which that discovery was put to use. There is definite information also as to the honors which came to Sequoya as a result of his discovery and as to the further service rendered by him to his people.

This is the story of one of our greatest Americans, who allowed no handicap to stand in his way. It is the story too of one who typifies the ideal of democracy: here was a man who accepted responsibility and believed service to his people of more importance than the mere acquiring of personal possessions.

The history of the Cherokee Nation during this period reveals our failure in the treatment of a minority group. It may be helpful in the avoiding of similar chapters in our own, and the world's future history.

Acknowledgments: This book undoubtedly came into being because of some chance remarks concerning the history of the Cherokee Nation made by Mr. D'Arcy McNickle of the Washington Office of Indian Affairs. For this, and his always helpful suggestions — including the loan of material on Keetoowah — as well as for reading the finished manuscript, my deep appreciation.

Anyone working with Cherokee material is continually conscious of the debt owed James Mooney, who, at the end of the nineteenth century, collected and translated a tremendous amount of manuscript written in the Sequoya syllabary, and who interviewed many Cherokees possessing recollections of an earlier period. Without his painstaking work this book of course could never have been written. The verses and formulas quoted throughout are from Mooney, permission having been obtained from the Smithsonian Institution, Bureau of American Ethnology.

Also this interpretation was greatly clarified by the published work of Grant Foreman, of Muskogee, Oklahoma, and of John Sparks Walker, of Chattanooga, Tennessee, authorities in their particular fields; both of whom were kind enough to read this manuscript and make valuable suggestions.

Acknowledgements for assistance are also due Dr. Alexander Wetmore, Dr. L. C. Harrington and Dr. M. W. Stirling of the Smithsonian Institution; Dr. William Harlan Gilbert, Donald Patterson, Frank E. Lorraine and David J. H. Cole of the Congressional Library; Miss Erma Hicks of the Chicago Office of Indian Affairs; Ruth Lapham Butler, The Newberry Library, Chicago. Miss Bess Glen and Miss Julia M. Bland of the National Archives; Dr. Adelaide L. Fries, Archivist, Moravian Church in America, Winston-Salem, North Carolina. Mr. and Mrs. George Owl of Norman, Oklahoma, furnished me the Cherokee names of the signers of the 1828 treaty. Miss Muriel H. Wright gave valuable suggestions.

For further information regarding Keetoowah I am indebted to Hon. Robert L. Owen; while Mr. and Mrs. Ezra Brainerd allowed me the generous use of books and publications from their library.

Washington, D.C., 1946

Selected Bibliography

Adair, James, *History of the American Indian,* ed. by Samuel Cole Williams, Watauga Press, Johnson City, Tenn., 1930.

Autrey, Hugh R., *New Echota, Birthplace of the American Indian Press,* National Park Service, Popular Study Series, History, No. 6, Government Printing Office, Washington, D.C., 1941.

Barce, Elmore, *Land of the Miamis,* Benton Review Shop, Fowler, Ind., 1927.

Bartram, William, *Travels Through North and South Carolina . . . the Cherokee Country,* James and Johnson, Philadelphia, 1791.

Observations on the Creek and Cherokee Indians, 1789, Preface by E. G. Squier, New York, 1851.

Bass, Althea, *Cherokee Messenger, Biography of Samuel Austin Worcester,* University of Oklahoma Press, Norman, Okla., 1936.

Bell, John, *Suppressed Report in relation to . . . . Cherokee Indians,* Washington, D.C., 1840.

Brown, John P., *Old Frontiers,* Southern Publications, Kingsport, Tenn., 1938.

Coulter, E. Merton, *A Short History of Georgia,* University of North Carolina Press, Chapel Hill, N.C., 1933.

Dale, Edward E. and Litton, Gaston, *Cherokee Cavaliers,* University of Oklahoma Press, Norman, Okla., 1939.

DeBo, Angie, *The Road to Disappearance,* University of Oklahoma Press, Norman, Okla., 1941.

Eaton, Rachel C., *John Ross and the Cherokee Indians,* George Banta Publishing Co., Menasha, Wis., 1914.

Foreman, Grant, *Indian Removal,* University of Oklahoma Press, Norman, Okla., 1943.

A History of Oklahoma, University of Oklahoma Press, Norman, Okla., 1942.

Sequoyah, University of Oklahoma Press, Norman, Okla., 1938.

The Five Civilized Tribes, University of Oklahoma Press, Norman, Okla., 1934.

Foster, George E., *Sequoyah,* Philadelphia, 1885.

Gabriel, George E., *Elias Boudinot, Cherokee, and His America,* University of Oklahoma Press, Norman, Okla., 1941.

Gilbert, William Harlan, *The Eastern Cherokees,* U.S. Bureau of American Ethnology, Bul. 133, Government Printing Office, Washington, D.C., 1943.

Hitchcock, Ethan Allen, *A Traveler in Indian Territory,* Ed. and Ann. by Grant Foreman, The Torch Press, Cedar Rapids, Ia., 1930.

Lumpkin, Wilson, *The Removal of the Cherokee Indians from Georgia,* Dodd, Mead & Co., 2 vols., New York, 1907.

McKinney, Thomas L. and Hall, James, *Indian Tribes of North America . . .* 3 vols., Ed. by Frederick Webb Hodge, John Grant, Publisher, Edinburgh, 1933.

Mooney, James, *The Cherokee Ball Play,* Judd & Detweiler, Washington, D.C., 1890.

Myths of the Cherokees, 19th Annual Report, U.S. Bureau of American Ethnology, Government Printing Office, Washington, D.C., 1900.

The Sacred Formulas of the Cherokees, 7th Annual Report, U.S. Bureau of American Ethnology, Government Printing Office, Washington, D.C., 1891.

and Olbrechts, Frans, *The Swimmer Manuscript,* Bureau of American Ethnology, Bul. 99, Government Printing Office, Washington, D.C., 1932.

Royce, Charles C., *The Cherokee Nation of Indians,* 5th Annual Report, U.S. Bureau of Ethnology, Government Printing Office, Washington, D.C., 1887.

Schwarze, Edmund, *History of the Moravian Missions Among Southern Indian Tribes . . .* Bethlehem Press, Bethlehem, Pa., 1923.

Smith, William H., *The St. Clair Papers,* R. Clark & Co., Cincinnati, O., 1882.

Starr, Emmet, *History of the Cherokee Indians . . .* The Warden Co., Oklahoma City, Okla., 1921.

U.S. Statutes at Large, Vol. 7, *Indian Treaties 1779–1842,* Chas. C. Little and James Brown, Boston, 1846.

Walker, Robert Sparks, *Torchlights to the Cherokees,* Macmillan, New York, 1931.

Washburn, Cephas, *Cherokees West, 1794–1839,* Emmet Starr, Publisher, Claremore, Okla., 1910.

Williams, Samuel Cole, *Early Travels in Tennessee Country, 1540–1800,* The Watauga Press, Johnson City, Tenn., 1928.

Wright, Muriel H. and Ward, Clara A., *Springplace Moravian Mission . . .* Cooperative Publishing Co., Guthrie, Okla., 1940.

The John Howard Payne Manuscript, Newberry Library, Chicago.

Chronicles of Oklahoma (Quarterly) Pub. by the Oklahoma Historical Society, 1921 to date.

Various Congressional Documents.

Harper's Magazine, May, 1870, *Sequoya* by W. A. Phillips.

The Keetoowah Society of the Oklahoma Cherokee (mimeographed pamphlet), Office of Indian Affairs, Washington, D.C.